GOLF
COLORADO ™

Complete Guide To Public Golf Courses

$7.95

Published by
Global Inc. Worldwide Marketing and Advertising

Publisher
James Dirk Durdy

Managing Editor
Barbara Ann Oldani

Art / Production Management
The Publishing Group, Veronika Clark

Contributing Writer
Barbara Ann Oldani

Cover
Arrowhead Golf Club, owned by National Golf Properties, operated by American Golf Corporation

Layout Designer
Barbara Ann Oldani

ISBN #1887430008

©1995 Global Inc. Worldwide Marketing and Advertising
All rights reserved. Reproduction in whole or part without written permission of Global Inc. is prohibited. Global Inc. Worldwide Marketing and Advertising, P.O. Box 2555, Littleton, CO 80161-2555, (303) 779-1001.

CONTENTS

INTRODUCTION

The experience of golfing in Colorado is like no other, anywhere. With unmatched velocity at unheard of elevations, your game is graced with virtually cloudless, cerulean skies, spring temperatures in the winter, dry air in the summer, majestic mountain backgrounds and wonderful Coloradoans.

The outstretched, still undisturbed plains, the spontaneously rolling yet urbanized front-range and the hypnotizing peaks of the Rocky Mountains themselves are all graced with courses unique to each terrain. Beautiful in every aspect, Colorado is a little slice of heaven to golfers.

Dedicated to those who treasure the spirit and excitement of playing golf in our little paradise, this guide is intended to provide you with pertinent as well as trivial information about the bountiful array of public golf courses in Colorado. Important facts such as course telephone numbers, addresses, pars, course ratings and green fees are furnished so your hunt for the perfect course can be made easier. We also list the names of those in charge, who designed the course, what year it opened and specific features that make each course unique from the others. Enhanced by a regional map at the beginning of each section, the information provided should enable you to find the perfect place to suit your special needs almost completely within the binding of this book.

The beginning of your search is just pages away. In fact, an important component is just to your right — the map of Colorado divided into regions. This guide is sanctioned off into segments containing golf courses found within their region. Under this main reference map you will find a listing of the cities with public golf courses under their region name. The regional contents begins on page six, giving you the page numbers for each region's index, as well as for each specific course. If you know the name of the course you want to view, it would be most convenient to flip to the back pages and find it listed alphabetically with its page number.

We hope this guide serves you completely throughout the 1995 season and into the new year, weather permitting.

Hidden treasures of Colorado golf abound, so get to it-

Enjoy!

James Dirk Durdy and Barbara Ann Oldani

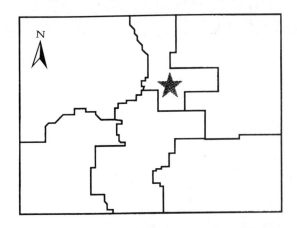

Regional Cities (Number Of Courses)

North Central (58)
Arvada (2)
Aurora (9)
Boulder (1)
Brighton (2)
Broomfield (1)
Denver (7)
Englewood (2)
Estes Park (1)
Evergreen (1)
Ft. Collins (7)
Golden (2)
Highland's Ranch (1)
Lafayette (1)
Lakewood (3)
Littleton (6)
Longmont (4)
Louisville (1)
Loveland (3)
Thornton (1)
Westminster (3)

South Central (20)
Alamosa (1)
Buena Vista (1)
Cañyon City (1)
Colorado Springs (9)
Crestone (1)
Florence (1)
Leadville (1)
Monte Vista (1)
Mosca (1)
Salida (1)
Westcliffe (1)

Southwest (13)
Cedaredge (1)
Cortez (1)
Crested Butte (1)
Delta (1)
Durango (3)
Gunnison (1)
Montrose (1)
Pagosa Springs (3)
Telluride (1)

Northwest (23)
Aspen (1)
Avon (2)
Battlement Mesa (1)
Breckenridge (1)
Copper Mountain (1)
Craig (1)
Edwards (1)
Fruita (1)
Glenwood Springs (2)
Grand Junction (2)
Grand Lake (1)
Keystone (1)
Meeker (1)
Rangley (1)
Rifle (1)
Silverthorne (1)
Snowmass (1)
Steamboat Springs (1)
Vail (1)

Northeast (16)
Akron (1)
Brush (1)
Burlington (1)
Cheyenne Wells(1)
Flagler (1)
Ft. Morgan (1)
Greeley (2)
Haxtun (1)
Holyoke (1)
Limon (1)
Milliken (1)
Sterling (1)
Stratton (1)
Wray (1)
Yuma (1)

Southeast (13)
Colorado City (3)
La Junta (1)
Lamar (1)
Las Animas (1)
La Veta (1)
Pueblo (2)
Pueblo West (1)
Rocky Ford (1)
Trinidad (1)

REGIONAL CONTENTS

(Continued on page 7)

REGIONAL CONTENTS

(Continued from page 6)

(Continued on page 8)

REGIONAL CONTENTS

(Continued from page ?)

Northwest Region   page 119

Northeast Region   page 145

(Continued on page 9)

REGIONAL CONTENTS

Colorado Golf Association

Serving Amateur Golf in Colorado Since 1912

Since 1912 the Colorado Golf Association (CGA) has been working to promote amateur golf in the state of Colorado. The CGA's first official function was to take over the administration of the state's amateur match play championship which began in 1901. This tournament (now known as the CGA Match Play Championship) is still conducted by the Colorado Golf Association, making it the oldest golf tournament in the state of Colorado. Since that time, the Colorado Golf Association has grown by leaps and bounds. The CGA now runs 20 state championships, has over 200 member clubs and more than 38,000 individual members.

Despite its growth, the CGA still exists to achieve the same goal it had in 1912: To promote amateur golf in Colorado. There are many ways the CGA promotes golf in the state of Colorado and many services we provide to our individual members ... here are just a few:

United States Golf Association (USGA) Handicap. The CGA administers the USGA Handicap System throughout the state and assures compliance with all system requirements. The CGA issues handicaps through the USGA's Golf Handicap and Information Network (GHIN), giving all its individual members access to the nation's largest handicap network.

Exceptional Tournament Score Reporting. In an effort to assure the accuracy of handicaps, the CGA collects and reports to all clubs the names of individuals who shoot exceptionally low scores in tournaments. This information helps handicap chairmen and tournament committees track the performance of their members and guarantee a level playing field for everyone.

Course Rating. The CGA rates courses at no charge in accordance with the USGA Course Rating System by evaluating obstacles and factors which affect the effective playing length of the course. The CGA then calculates and publishes Course Ratings and Slope Ratings for all Colorado courses.

Course Pace Rating. Slow play is an issue that every golf course is concerned with. The CGA gathers data and performs calculations to provide each course with a USGA Pace Rating (recommended amount of time to play each hole and a full 18-hole round). This Pace Rating sets a realistic goal for the amount of time it should take to play every course in the state. This Pace Rating can be used by the club to effectively manage the pace-of-play issue at their club.

Junior Golf. The Colorado Junior Golf Association (CJGA) is a division of the Colorado Golf Association and exists to support junior golf programs for both boys and girls, 18 years of age and

(Continued on page 11)

Colorado Golf Association

(Continued from page 10)

under. CJGA provides clinics, supervised practice and competitions during the golf season, conducts a volunteer work program, a caddie program, holds a Drive-Pitch-Putt competition and conducts rules and etiquette seminars.

Hall Of Fame. The CGA works closely with the Colorado Golf Hall of Fame to recognize and honor individuals who have made outstanding contributions to golf in Colorado and to research and collect the information and items necessary to create, maintain and display a history of Colorado Golf.

Eisenhower-Evans Scholarship. The CGA funds the Eisenhower-Evans Scholarship program at the University of Colorado by selling bag tags and Par Club memberships and conducting the annual Par Club Tournament. This program was established in Colorado in 1963 to send deserving caddies to college. Since its inception more than 225 Eisenhower-Evans Scholars have graduated from the program and 35 more are currently living in the chapter house in Boulder. The program is administered by the Evans Scholars Foundation through the Western Golf Association.

Rules. The CGA serves as the state authority on the Rules of Golf and conducts Rules clinics and seminars for volunteers and member clubs.

Statistics. The CGA responds to a myriad of inquiries regarding golf operations and development. The CGA helps document the interests of golf by maintaining a data base useful in responding to questions about rounds played, costs, consumer spending, need for more facilities, projects planned or under construction, etc.

Playing Conditions. The CGA supports turfgrass and other golf-related research and encourages and helps schedule USGA Turf Advisory Service visits to member clubs.

Capital Development Fund. The CGA sets aside a portion of each individual member's annual fee for future development and operation of a golf facility and "Colorado Golf House".

These are only some of the many ways the Colorado Golf Association strives to achieve its goal of promoting golf in the state of Colorado. No matter what your ability, rest assured that the CGA is working hard to make the game of golf more enjoyable for everyone with a passion for the game of a lifetime!

Colorado Women's Golf Association

Changing Women's Approaches To The Game Of Golf

Gone are the days when the only clubs being swung by women on grass were croquet mallets. Today it is quite a rare occurrence to see a woman standing on a large, green plain, wearing a flowing white skirt, matching sweater, sipping lemonade trying to get an oversized wood ball through a raised arch.

The year is 1995 and women make up a significant portion of some of the most talented and accomplished golfers in the world. The Colorado Women's Golf Association (CWGA) is a non-profit organization dedicated to promoting and conserving the best interests and true spirit of the game of golf for women in the state of Colorado. Founded in 1916, the CWGA is comprised of golf clubs with individual members.

Members join the CWGA through their golf club and pay a fee to enjoy a plethora of benefits, some of which are:

.a USGA/GHIN handicap index, updated periodically

.a rating committee which provides systematic course ratings, in accordance with USGA policies

.a rules committee which provides the application of the USGA Rules of Golf at CWGA Championships and other tournaments, as well as offers regional workshops and club seminars on the USGA Rules of Golf, including up-to-date revisions and changes

.an extensive CWGA tournament schedule which provides state-level competitions: 3 state championships, 2 junior championships, 3 four-ball championships and 2 mixed championships

For more information and complete listing of the endless benefits, the CWGA can be contacted by mail, phone and fax:

5655 South Yosemite, Suite 101
Englewood, Colorado 80111

Phone: (303) 220-5456, (800) 392-CWGA

Fax: (303) 290-0593

TOURNAMENT LISTING

Tournament	Dates	Location
CJGA Fundraiser Celebration Tournament	5/1	Plum Creek Golf & C.C.
CGA/CWGA Mixed Stableford Team Champ.	5/13-14	Grandote Golf & Country Club
CJGA Caddie School	5/21	Bear Creek Golf Club
US Open Local Qualifying	5/22	Ptarmigan Golf & C.C.
CGA Net Two-Man Team Championship	5/23-25	Lake Valley Golf Course
CGA Senior Match Play Championship	5/30-6/3	Riverdale Dunes Golf Course
US Women's Amateur Public Links Qual.	6/1	Englewood Golf Course
US Open Sectional Qualifying	6/5	Columbine Courntry Club
CGA/CJGA Boy's Junior Match Play Champ.	6/5-8	Bear Creek Golf Club
CJGA (11-13) Tour Tournament	6/6	The Links Golf Course
CWGA Brassie Champ. Four-Ball Stroke Pl.	6/6-7	Pine Creek Golf Course
CJGA (10 & Under) Tour Tournament	6/7	Foothills Golf Club Par-3
CJGA Learning-to-Play Practice	6/8	Harvard Gulch Golf Course
CGA Parent-Child Championship	6/10-11	Grandote Golf & Country Club
US Senior Open Sectional Qualifying	6/12	Cherry Hills Country Club
CJGA (14-18) Tour Tournament	6/12	Riverdale Knolls Golf Course
CWGA Junior Stroke Play Championship	6/13-15	Lake Arbor Golf Club
CJGA (14-18) Tour Tournament	6/14	South Suburban Golf Course
CJGA Learning-to-Play Practice	6/15	Harvard Gulch Golf Course
CGA Senior Two-Man Team Championship	6/16-18	Pagosa Pines Golf Club
CJGA (14-18) Tour Tournament	6/19	Denver City Park Golf Course
CJGA (14-18) Western MiniTour	6/19-21	Adobe Creek Golf Course
CJGA (14-18) Western MiniTour	6/19-21	Tiara Rado Golf Course
CJGA (14-18) Western MiniTour	6/19-21	Montrose Golf Course
Women's Western Golf Ass. Am. Match Play	6/19-24	The Links at North Fork
CJGA (11-13) Tour Tournament	6/20	Springhill Golf Course
US Women's Open Qualifying	6/21	The Broadmoor East Golf Crs
CJGA (10 & Under) Tour Tournament	6/21	Northridge Pitch 'n' Putt
US Women's Am. Public Links Match Play	6/21-25	Hominy Hills Golf Course, NJ
CJGA Learning-to-Play Practice	6/22	Harvard Gulch Golf Course
US Amateur Public Links Sectional Qual.	6/23-24	Legacy Ridge Golf Course
CGA Public Links Championship	6/23-25	Legacy Ridge Golf Course
CJGA (11-13) Tour Tournament	6/26	Foothills Exec-9 Golf Course
CJGA (14-18) Tour Tournament	6/27	Collindale Golf Course
CGA Two-Man Team Championship	6/27-29	Hyland Hills Golf Course
CJGA (10 & Under) Tour Tournament	6/28	Greenway Park Golf Course
CJGA (11-13) Tour Tournament	6/28	Sunset Golf Course
CWGA Senior Stroke Play Championship	6/28-29	Eaton Country Club
CJGA (14-18) Tour Tournament	6/29	Aurora Hills Golf Club
CJGA Learning-to-Play Practice	6/29	Harvard Gulch Golf Course
CJGA (10 & Under) Tour Tournament	7/5	Boulder Country Club Par-3
US Junior Boys' Amateru Qualifying	7/5-6	Eagle Golf Club
CGA/CJGA Boy's Junior Stroke Play Champ	7/5-7	Eagle Golf Club
CJGA Learning-to-Play Practice	7/6	Harvard Gulch Golf Course
CJGA (11-13) Tour Tournament	7/10	Indian Tree Golf Course
CJGA (14-18) Tour Tournament	7/10	Green Gables Country Club
CGA Match Play Championship	7/10-16	Thorncreek Golf Club
CJGA (14-18) Tour Tournament	7/11	Eaton Country Club
CJGA (11-13) Tour Tournament	7/12	The Meadows Golf Club
CJGA Learning-to-Play Practice	7/13	Harvard Gulch Golf Course
US Women's Open	7/13-16	The Broadmoor Golf Club
CJGA (10 & Under) Tour Tournament	7/14	Windsor Gardens Golf Club
CJGA (11-13) Tour Tournament	7/17	Colorado Springs C.C.
CJGA (14-18) Southern MiniTour	7/17-19	Walking Stick Golf Course
CJGA (14-18) Southern MiniTour	7/17-19	Hollydot Golf Course
CJGA (14-18) Southern MiniTour	7/17-19	Pueblo West Golf Club

(Continued on page 14)

TOURNAMENT LISTING

(Continued from page 13)

Tournament	Dates	Location
CWGA Junior Match Play Championship	7/17-20	Foothills Golf Course
Women's Western Golf Ass. Junior Amateur	7/17-21	Conway Farms Golf Course, IL
CJGA (10 & Under) Tour Tournament	7/19	Indian Tree Golf Course Par-3
CJGA Learning-to-Play Practice	7/20	Harvard Gulch Golf Course
Daily Sentinel/CGA Western Chap Junior Ch	7/24-26	Adobe Creek Golf Course
Daily Sentinel/CGA Western Chap Junior Ch	7/24-26	Lincoln Park Golf Course
Daily Sentinel/CGA Western Chap Junior Ch	7/24-26	Bookcliff Country Club
Daily Sentinel/CGA Western Chap Junior Ch	7/24-26	Tirara Rado Golf Course
US Women's Amateur Qualifying	7/25	Glenmoor Country Club
CJGA (11-13) Tour Tournament	7/25	City Park Golf Course
CJGA (10 & Under) Tour Tournament	7/26	Centre Hills Golf Club
CJGA (14-18) Tour Tournament	7/26	Twin Peaks Golf Course
CJGA Learning-to-Play Practice	7/27	Harvard Gulch Golf Course
CJGA (10 & Under) Tour Tournament	7/28	South Suburban GC Par-3
CGA Storke Play Qualifying	7/29	Yampa Valley Golf Club
CGA Western Chapter Championship	7/29-30	Yampa Valley Golf Club
CGA Stroke Play Qualifying	7/31	Gleneagle Golf Club
CGA Stroke Play Qualifying	7/31	The Meadows Golf Club
CJGA (11-13) Tour Tournament	7/31	Evergreen Golf Course
CJGA (14-18) Tour Tournament	7/31	Eisenhower Silver Golf Club
US Girls' Junior Championship Match Play	7/31-8/5	Longmeadow C.C., MA
CGA Senior Stroke Play Championship	8/1-3	Mira Vista Golf Course
CJGA (14-18) Askins Memorial Team	8/2	Meridian Golf Club
CJGA Learning-to-Play Practice	8/3	Harvard Gulch Golf Course
US Amateur Qualifying	8/7	Boulder Country Club
CJGA (10 & Under) Tour Tournament	8/7	Southglenn Country Club
CJGA (11-13) Tour Tournament	8/7	Denver Country Club
CWGA Match Play Championship	8/7-10	Thorncreek Golf Club
US Women's Amateur Match Play Format	8/7-12	The Country Club, MA
CJGA (11-13) Tour Tournament	8/8	Pinery Country Club
CJGA (10 & Under) Tour Tournament	8/9	Harvard Gulch Golf Course
CJGA Learning-to-Play Practice	8/10	Harvard Gulch Golf Course
CGA Stroke Play Championship	8/10-13	West Woods Golf Club
CJGA (11-13) Tour Tournament	8/14	Heather Gardens Golf Course
CJGA (10 & Under) Tour Tournament	8/16	Kennedy Golf Course Par-3
CJGA Learning-to-Play Tournament	8/17	Harvard Gulch Golf Course
CWGA Stroke Play Championship	8/22-24	Boulder Country Club
US Mid-Amateur Qualifying	8/28	Plum Creek Golf & C.C.
CGA Mid-Amateur Qualifying	9/6	Englewood Golf Course
CGA Mid-Amateur Qualifying	9/6	Ft. Carson Golf Course
CGA Mid-Amateur Qualifying	9/6	Bookcliff Country Club
USGA Senior Amateur Qualifying	9/7	Fox Hollow Golf Club
CGA Senior Four-Ball Championship	9/12-14	Battlement Mesa Golf Club
CGA/CWGA Mixed Team Championship	9/16-17	Sheraton Steamboat Resort
CGA Mid-Amateur Championship	9/22-24	Ft. Collins Country Club
US Women's Mid Amateur Qualifying	8/30	Columbine Country Club
CWGA Mashie Champ. Better Ball Match Pl.	9/5-7	Arrowhead Golf Club
US Senior Women's Amateur	9/13-15	Sommerset Country Club, MN
CGA/CWGA Mixed Team Championship	9/16-17	Sheraton Steamboat Resort
CWGA 4-Ball Stroke Play Champ. for 9-Hole	9/18	Green Gables Country Club
US Women's Mid-Amateur Match Play	9/18-23	Essex Country Club, MA
CGA Public Links Team Championship	10/1	TBA
Women's Western Golf Ass. Senior Amateur	10/2-4	Turnberry Isle Resort, FL
CJGA Tournament of Champions	10/7-8	Fox Hollow Golf Club
Par Club Tournament	10/9	TBA

Association Of Disabled American Golfers	(303) 220-0921
Colorado Golf Association	(303) 779-GOLF
outside Denver	(800) 228-4675
Colorado Golf Foundation	(303) 799-GOLF
Colorado Golf Hall Of Fame	(303) 799-GOLF
Colorado Golf Resort Association	(303) 699-4653
<u>Colorado Golfer</u> Newspaper	(303) 699-4653
Colorado High School Activities Association	(303) 344-5050
Colorado Junior Golf Association	(303) 799-GOLF
Colorado Open	(303) 830-0137
Colorado Section, PGA Of America	(303) 745-3697
Colorado Women's Golf Association	(303) 220-5456
outside Denver	(800) 392-2942
Denver International Airport Information	(303) 342-2000
	(800) AIR-2-DEN
Denver International Airport Paging	(303) 342-2300
Golf 4 Fun	(303) 985-5851
	(303) 988-8133
The International	(303) 688-6000
National Golf Foundation	(407) 744-6006
publications / membership	(800) 733-6006
Professional Golf Association Of America	(407) 624-8400
Professional Golf Association Section Office	(303) 745-3697
Professional Golf Association Tour Office	(904) 285-3700
Professional Golf Association West	(619) 546-7100
Rocky Mtn. Golf Course Superintendent Ass.	(303) 688-2267
United States Golf Association	(908) 234-2300
Western Golf Association	(708) 724-4600

FUN FACTS

Did You Know????

As a golfer, you are one of almost **25 million** people over the age of 11 playing approximately **499 million** rounds of golf a year in the United States - if you each play only 18 holes per year (yah right), that's **eight billion, 982 million holes!** Imagine the balls -

Thanks to the wonderfully thin, dry air in Colorado, golf balls hit here soar to significantly longer distances than they do when they're hit at lower altitudes. To the novice, and sometimes not-so-novice, high-elevation golfer, these unhinged distance shots frequently don't travel across the appropriate fairway or on to the next green. The extra strokes, slices, ball hunts and colorful remarks that take place atop this fair state can in no way hurt the already colossal golf ball industry. Thanks to your many blunders into water hazards and unchartered, feet-thick rough, the people who make the balls do so to the tune of **$560 cool million** in sales per year. One dozen of the top four manufacturer's golf balls range in price from **$20** to **$60**. All of you flailers had better have your check books ready.

Well, never fear. Golf is an awe-inspiring sport, and the awe-inspiring people at the Colorado Golf Association have a hot-line to help you in your times of need. By dialing **779-4653** in Denver or **1-800-228-4675** outside Denver, their staff will answer all sorts of questions relating to golf. Kind of the "411" for golfers.

Having a handicap isn't usually something for which most would aspire, but in the sport of golf it is in fact an honor. A handicap is only bequeathed to those who are **members** or **associate members of golf clubs**. Once a member, to acquire a **handicap** your scoring ability is compared to the scoring abilities of expert amateurs. **You must golf on courses of standard difficulty** and report **only 20 scores, your best from a given number of rounds**. Once you've accomplished this, an index is used to don upon you, a **handicap**. Of course, there's more to it, but that's what that hot-line is for.

Handicap or no handicap, golfers as a whole play and/or support the game to achieve some level of greatness. Colorado's greatest of these contributors are inducted into the **Colorado Golf Hall of Fame**. For the past 22 years this Hall of Fame, located at 5655 South Yosemite in Englewood, has been honoring men and women for the instrumental parts

Golf Colorado, page 17

NORTH CENTRAL REGION

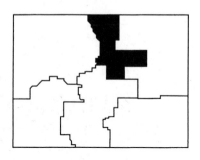

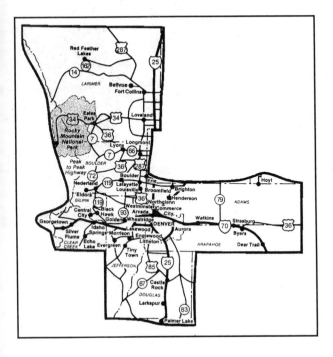

North Central Region

Applewood Golf Course

Address: 14001 West 32nd Avenue
Golden, CO 80401

Phone #: (303) 279-3003
Tee Times: (303) 279-3003

Tee Time Info: (resident):   5 day advance
    (non-resident): 5 day advance

Green Fees: (resident): $19.00 weekday
    $21.00 weekend
    (non-resident): $19.00 weekday
    $21.00 weekend
Credit Cards: Master Card, Visa, American Express
Discounts: seniors, twilight

Number of Holes: 18
Number of Courses on Site: 1

	Championship Tees	Men's Tees	Ladies' Tees
Par:	71	71	71
Length:	6229	5975	5349
Course Rating:	68.3	67.2	69.0
Slope:	120	114	109

Year Opened: 1955

Golf Carts Available: yes   **Cart Fee:** $9.50 per player
Driving Range: yes
On Site Lodging: no

Tournaments: yes

Annual Number of Golf Days: 344
Total Rounds Played Annually: 72,300

General Manager: Byron Finnefrock
Head Pro: Ray Olson

Designer/Architect:
Average Play Time: 3:47
Special Features: clubhouse, pro shop, snack bar

Arrowhead Golf Club

Address: 10850 West SundownTrail
Littleton, CO 80125

Phone #: (303) 973-9614
Tee Times: (303) 973-9614

Tee Time Info: (resident): 7 day advance
(non-resident): 7 day advance

Green Fees: (resident): $71.00 weekday
$81.00 weekend
(non-resident): $71.00 weekday
$81.00 weekend
Credit Cards: Master Card, Visa, American Express
Discounts: low season, twilight

Number of Holes: 18
Number of Courses on Site: 1

	Championship Tees	Men's Tees	Ladies' Tees
Par:	70	70	72
Length:	6682	6269	5465
Course Rating:	70.9	68.9	70.0
Slope:	134	129	123

Year Opened: 1972

Golf Carts Available: yes **Cart Fee:** $10.68
Driving Range: yes
On Site Lodging: no

Tournaments: yes

Annual Number of Golf Days: 240
Total Rounds Played Annually: 42,000

General Manager: Gordon Tolbert
Head Pro: Gordon Tolbert
Superintendent: Roe Sherbert

Designer/Architect: Robert Trent Jones, Jr.
Average Play Time: 4:21
Special Features: one of America's top 75 public courses, Golf Digest

Aurora Hills Golf Course

Address: 50 South Peoria Street
Aurora, CO 80012

Phone #: (303) 364-6611
Tee Times: (303) 397-1818

Tee Time Info: **(resident):** 5 day advance
(non-resident): 3 day advance

Green Fees:

	(resident):	$13.00 weekday
		$14.00 weekend
	(non-resident):	$18.00 weekday
		$20.00 weekend

Credit Cards: Master Card, Visa
Discounts: seniors

Number of Holes: 18
Number of Courses on Site: 1

	Championship Tees	Men's Tees	Ladies' Tees
Par:	72	72	73
Length:	6735	6446	5919
Course Rating:	70.0	68.8	74.6
Slope:	115	112	116

Year Opened: 1969

Golf Carts Available: yes   **Cart Fee:** $18
Driving Range: yes
On Site Lodging: no

Tournaments: yes

Annual Number of Golf Days: 335
Total Rounds Played Annually: 65,500

General Manager: Mike McCutchen
Head Pro: Mike McCutchen
Superintendent: Walter Shultz

Designer/Architect: Henry Hughes
Average Play Time: 3:49
Special Features: putting green, restaurant, bar

Cattail Creek Golf Course

Address: 2116 West 29th
Loveland, CO 80538

Phone #:   (970) 663-5310
Tee Times: (970) 669-5800

Tee Time Info: (resident):   5 day advance
(non-resident): 5 day advance

Green Fees: (resident): $7.00

(non-resident): $7.00

Credit Cards: no
Discounts: senior, junior

Number of Holes: 9
Number of Courses on Site: 1

	Championship Tees	Men's Tees	Ladies' Tees
Par:	27	27	27
Length:	1426	1175	973
Course Rating:	no rating	no rating	no rating
Slope:	no record	no record	no record

Year Opened: 1992

Golf Carts Available: yes   **Cart Fee:** $7.00
Driving Range: yes
On Site Lodging: no

Tournaments: yes

Annual Number of Golf Days: 300

General Manager: Rod Chapman
Head Pro: Mike Sloan
Superintendent: David Cumpsten

Average Play Time: 1:30
Special Features: putting green, snack bar

Centennial Golf Club

Address: 5800 South Federal Boulevard
Littleton, CO 80123

Phone #:   (303) 794-5838
Tee Times: (303) 794-5838

Tee Time Info: (resident):   1 day advance (weekdays), 5 1/2 (weekends)
(non-resident):   1 day advance (weekdays), 2-3 (weekends)

Green Fees: **(resident):** $8.00

    (non-resident): $11.50

Credit Cards: Master Card, Visa, Discover
Discounts: seniors

Number of Holes: 9
Number of Courses on Site: 1

	Championship Tees	Men's Tees	Ladies' Tees
Par:	31	31	31
Length:	2143	1908	1697
Course Rating:	62.6	60.6	58.4
Slope:	96	93	88

Year Opened: 1986

Golf Carts Available: yes   **Cart Fee:** $18.00
Driving Range: yes
On Site Lodging: no

Tournaments: yes

Annual Number of Golf Days: 302
Total Rounds Played Annually: 35,000

General Manager: South Suburban Metro Parks And Rec. District
Head Pro: Terry Cahl
Superintendent: Bud Ducey

Designer/Architect: Dick Phelps
Average Play Time: 3:04
Special Features: pro shop, indoor tennis, snack bar

Centre Hills Golf Club

Address: 16300 East Centretech Parkway
Aurora, CO

Phone #: (303) 343-4935
Tee Times: (303) 343-4935

Tee Time Info: (resident): advance tee times not available
(non-resident): advance tee times not available

Green Fees: (resident): $5.00 weekday
$5.50 weekend
(non-resident): $6.75 weekday
$8.00 weekend
Credit Cards: Master Card, Visa, Discover
Discounts: seniors, juniors

Number of Holes: 9
Number of Courses on Site: 1

	Championship Tees	Men's Tees	Ladies' Tees
Par:	no	27	27
Length:	no	1330	1150
Course Rating:	no	no rating	no rating
Slope:	no	no record	no record

Year Opened: 1988

Golf Carts Available: no
Driving Range: yes
On Site Lodging: no

Tournaments: yes

Annual Number of Golf Days: 300
Total Rounds Played Annually: 42,500

General Manager: Bob McNamee
Head Pro: Bob McNamee
Superintendent: Doug Duncan

Designer/Architect: Dick Phelps
Average Play Time: 1:00
Special Features: pro shop

City Park Golf Course

Address: 2500 York Street
Denver, CO 80205

Phone #: (303) 295-2095
Tee Times: (303) 784-4000

Tee Time Info: (resident): 5 day advance
(non-resident): 3 day advance

Green Fees: **(resident):** $13.50 weekday
$14.50 weekend
(non-resident): $18.75 weekday
$19.75 weekend

Credit Cards: no
Discounts: seniors, juniors

Number of Holes: 18
Number of Courses on Site: 1

	Championship Tees	Men's Tees	Ladies' Tees
Par:	72	72	72
Length:	6858	6509	6181
Course Rating:	67.8	67.8	73.3
Slope:	105	105	116

Year Opened: 1920

Golf Carts Available: yes   **Cart Fee:** $20.00
Driving Range: yes
On Site Lodging: no

Tournaments: yes

Annual Number of Golf Days: 301
Total Rounds Played Annually: 57,633

General Manager: Sam Taylor
Head Pro: Tom Bacon

Average Play Time: 4:20
Special Features: pro shop, putting green, chipping green, restaurant

City Park Nine Golf Course

Address: 411 South Bryan Avenue
Fort Collins, CO 80521

Phone #: (970) 221-6650
Tee Times: (970) 221-6650

Tee Time Info: (resident): 3 day advance
(non-resident): 3 day advance

Green Fees: (resident): $15.00

(non-resident): $15.00

Credit Cards: Master Card, Visa
Discounts: juniors

Number of Holes: 9
Number of Courses on Site: 1

	Championship Tees	Men's Tees	Ladies' Tees
Par:	no	72	72
Length:	no	6364	5472
Course Rating:	no	68.0	70.8
Slope:	no	114	121

Year Opened: 1940

Golf Carts Available: yes   **Cart Fee:** $16.00
Driving Range: yes
On Site Lodging: no

Tournaments: yes

Annual Number of Golf Days: 283
Total Rounds Played Annually: 43,000

General Manager: Jerry P. Brown
Head Pro: Jim Greer
Superintendent: David Sadler

Designer/Architect: W.P.A.
Average Play Time: 3:38
Special Features: clubhouse, pro shop

Coal Creek Golf Course

Address: 585 West Dillon Road
Louisville, CO 80027

Phone #: (303) 666-7888
Tee Times: (303) 666-7888

Tee Time Info: (resident): 4 day advance
(non-resident): 3 day advance

Green Fees: **(resident):** $14 weekday
$16 weekend
(non-resident): $20 weekday
$22 weekend
Credit Cards: Master Card, Visa
Discounts: twilight

Number of Holes: 18
Number of Courses on Site: 1

	Championship Tees	Men's Tees	Ladies' Tees
Par:	72	72	72
Length:	6957	6593	5168
Course Rating:	71.1	70.1	68.4
Slope:	130	128	114

Year Opened: 1990

Golf Carts Available: yes   **Cart Fee:** $18
Driving Range: yes
On Site Lodging: no

Tournaments: no

Annual Number of Golf Days: 280
Total Rounds Played Annually: 57,000

General Manager: John Ott
Head Pro: John Ott
Superintendent: Tom Kramlich

Designer/Architect: Dick Phelps
Average Play Time: 4:07
Special Features: restaurant, practice facility

Collindale Golf Course

Address: 1441 East Horsetooth Road
Fort Collins, CO 80525

Phone #: (970) 221-6651
Tee Times: (970) 221-6651

Tee Time Info: (resident): 3 day advance
(non-resident): 3 day advance

Green Fees: **(resident):** $10.00 weekday
$15.00 weekend
(non-resident): $10.00 weekday
$15.00 weekend
Credit Cards: Master Card, Visa
Discounts: low season, juniors

Number of Holes: 18
Number of Courses on Site: 1

	Championship Tees	Men's Tees	Ladies' Tees
Par:	71	71	73
Length:	7011	6403	5472
Course Rating:	71.5	69.3	69.9
Slope:	126	120	113

Year Opened: 1971

Golf Carts Available: yes   **Cart Fee:** $18.00
Driving Range: yes
On Site Lodging: no

Tournaments: yes

Annual Number of Golf Days: 302
Total Rounds Played Annually: 66,000

General Manager: Joe Nance
Head Pro: Joe Nance
Superintendent: Doug Evans

Designer/Architect: Frank Hummel
Average Play Time: 3:57
Special Features: pro shop, restaurant

Eagle Golf Club

Address: 1200 Clubhouse Drive
Broomfield, CO 80020

Phone #: (303) 466-3322
Tee Times: (303) 466-3322

Tee Time Info: (resident): first priority
(non-resident): 4 day advance

Green Fees: (resident): $20.00 weekday
$25.00 weekend
(non-resident): $20.00 weekday
$25.00 weekend
Credit Cards: Master Card, Visa
Discounts: seniors

Number of Holes: 18
Number of Courses on Site: 1

	Championship Tees	Men's Tees	Ladies' Tees
Par:	71	71	73
Length:	6609	6202	5745
Course Rating:	69.7	68.1	71.4
Slope:	117	116	122

Year Opened: 1970, 1984

Golf Carts Available: yes   **Cart Fee:** $20.00
Driving Range: yes
On Site Lodging: no

Tournaments: yes

Annual Number of Golf Days: 312
Total Rounds Played Annually: 50,000

General Manager: Mark Bryant
Head Pro: Mark Bryant

Designer/Architect: Dick Phelps
Average Play Time: 3:49
Special Features: pro shop, restaurant

Englewood Municipal Golf Course

Address: 2101 West Oxford
                 Englewood, CO 80110

Phone #:   (303) 761-0848
Tee Times: (303) 761-0848

Tee Time Info: (resident):   3 day advance
                (non-resident): 2 day advance

Green Fees: (resident): $12.00

               (non-resident): $18.00

Credit Cards: Master Card, Visa
Discounts: no

Number of Holes: 18
Number of Courses on Site: 1

	Championship Tees	Men's Tees	Ladies' Tees
Par:	72	72	72
Length:	6836	6487	5967
Course Rating:	71.1	69.4	72.2
Slope:	126	120	120

Year Opened: 1977, 1982

Golf Carts Available: yes   **Cart Fee:** $19.00
Driving Range: yes
On Site Lodging: no

Tournaments: yes

Annual Number of Golf Days: 300
Total Rounds Played Annually: 65,182

General Manager: Bob Burgener
Head Pro: Michael Bickens
Superintendent: David Lee

Designer/Architect: Phelps - Benz
Average Play Time: 3:59
Special Features: bar, restaurant, mini-golf, go-cart track, pro shop

Estes Park Golf Course

Address: 1080 South St. Vrain Avenue
P.O. Box 1379
Estes Park, CO 80517
Phone #: (970) 586-8146
Tee Times: (970) 586-8146

Tee Time Info: (resident): 7 day advance
(non-resident): 7 day advance

Green Fees: (resident): $26.00

(non-resident): $26.00

Credit Cards: Master Card, Visa
Discounts: low season, twilight

Number of Holes: 18
Number of Courses on Site: 1

	Championship Tees	Men's Tees	Ladies' Tees
Par:	71	71	74
Length:	6326	5869	5869
Course Rating:	68.3	66.2	71.7
Slope:	118	109	121

Year Opened: 1917, 1991

Golf Carts Available: yes   **Cart Fee:** $20.00
Driving Range: yes
On Site Lodging: no

Tournaments: yes

Annual Number of Golf Days: 230
Total Rounds Played Annually: 26,800

General Manager: Skip Peck
Head Pro: Skip Peck

Designer/Architect: Henry Hughes, Dick Phelps
Average Play Time: 3:49
Special Features: pro shop, full practice facility, restaurant, lounge

Evergreen Golf Course

Address: 29614 Upper Bear Creek Road
Evergreen, CO 80439

Phone #: (303) 674-6351 *※ Tee times @ this*
Tee Times: (303) 784-4000 *# too.*

Tee Time Info: (resident): 5 day advance
(non-resident): 3 day advance

Green Fees: **(resident):** $13.50 weekday
$14.50 weekend
(non-resident): $18.75 weekday
$19.75 weekend

Credit Cards: no
Discounts: yes

Number of Holes: 18
Number of Courses on Site: 1

	Championship Tees	Men's Tees	Ladies' Tees
Par:	no	69	69
Length:	no	5100	4494
Course Rating:	no	61.6	63.7
Slope:	no	102	103

Year Opened: 1926

Golf Carts Available: yes   **Cart Fee:** $20.00
Driving Range: no
On Site Lodging: no

Tournaments: yes

Annual Number of Golf Days: 300
Total Rounds Played Annually: 35,000

General Manager: Bob Bittinger
Head Pro: Ted Parker
Superintendent: Steve Atinrich

Average Play Time: 4:00
Special Features: pro shop, restaurant

Flatirons Golf Course

Address: 5706 East Arapahoe Road
P.O. Box 791
Boulder, CO 80306
Phone #: (303) 442-7851
Tee Times: (303)442-7851

Tee Time Info: (resident): 1 day advance (weekdays), 3 1/2 (weekends)
(non-resident): 1 day advance (weekdays), 3 1/2 (weekends)

Green Fees: (resident): $14.00

(non-resident): $17.50

Credit Cards: soon
Discounts: seniors, juniors

Number of Holes: 18
Number of Courses on Site: 1

	Championship Tees	Men's Tees	Ladies' Tees
Par:	70	70	71
Length:	6765	6346	5615
Course Rating:	69.9	68.5	75.0
Slope:	125	122	126

Year Opened: 1929

Golf Carts Available: yes   **Cart Fee:** $18.00
Driving Range: yes
On Site Lodging: no

Tournaments: yes

Annual Number of Golf Days: 267
Total Rounds Played Annually: 60,000

General Manager: Chase Weir
Head Pro: Doug Cook
Superintendent: Dave Brown

Designer/Architect: Robert Bruce Harris
Average Play Time: 3:53
Special Features: mountain views of spectacular Flatirons

Foothills Golf Course

Address: 3901 South Carr Street
Denver, CO 80235

Phone #: (303) 989-3901
Tee Times: (303) 989-3901

Tee Time Info: (resident): 3 day advance
(non-resident): 2 day advance

Green Fees: **(resident):** $14.75

(non-resident): $20.00

Credit Cards: Master Card, Visa
Discounts: seniors

Number of Holes: 18
Number of Courses on Site: 3

	Championship Tees	Men's Tees	Ladies' Tees
Par:	72	72	74
Length:	6908	6497	6028
Course Rating:	71.1	69.1	73.4
Slope:	122	116	118

Year Opened: 1972

Golf Carts Available: yes   **Cart Fee:** $20.00
Driving Range: yes
On Site Lodging: no

Tournaments: yes

Annual Number of Golf Days: 285
Total Rounds Played Annually: 131,562

General Manager: Dan Hylton
Head Pro: Jim Hajek

Designer/Architect: Dick Phelps
Average Play Time: 3:53
Special Features: pro shop, restaurant, par 3 course, executive 9

Fox Hollow - Canyon Links Course

Address: 13410 West Morrison Road
Lakewood, CO 80228

Phone #: (303) 986-7888
Tee Times: (303) 986-7888

Tee Time Info: (resident): 7 day advance
(non-resident): 6 day advance

Green Fees: (resident): $22.00

(non-resident): $27.00

Credit Cards: Master Card, Visa
Discounts: seniors, juniors

Number of Holes: 18
Number of Courses on Site: 3

	Championship Tees	Men's Tees	Ladies' Tees
Par:	71	71	71
Length:	7030	6745	5461
Course Rating:	72.3	70.9	71.6
Slope:	134	128	124

Year Opened: 1993

Golf Carts Available: yes   **Cart Fee:** $10 per player
Driving Range: yes
On Site Lodging: no

Tournaments: yes

Annual Number of Golf Days: 280
Total Rounds Played Annually: 82,000

General Manager: Craig Parzybok
Head Pro: Craig Parzybok
Superintendent: Don Tolson

Designer/Architect: Denis Griffiths
Average Play Time: 4:08
Special Features: clubhouse, practice green, chipping green

Fox Hollow - Meadow Links Course

Address: 13410 West Morrison Road
Lakewood, CO 80228

Phone #: (303) 986-7888
Tee Times: (303) 986-7888

Tee Time Info: (resident): 7 day advance
(non-resident): 6 day advance

Green Fees: (resident): $22.00

(non-resident): $27.00

Credit Cards: Master Card, Visa
Discounts: seniors, juniors

Number of Holes: 18
Number of Courses on Site: 3

	Championship Tees	Men's Tees	Ladies' Tees
Par:	72	72	72
Length:	6888	6639	5396
Course Rating:	71.9	70.7	71.5
Slope:	132	127	119

Year Opened: 1993

Golf Carts Available: yes   **Cart Fee:** $10 per player
Driving Range: yes
On Site Lodging: no

Tournaments: yes

Annual Number of Golf Days: 280
Total Rounds Played Annually: 82,000

General Manager: Craig Parzybok
Head Pro: Craig Parzybok
Superintendent: Don Tolson

Designer/Architect: Denis Griffiths
Average Play Time: 4:08
Special Features: clubhouse, practice green, chipping green

Fox Hollow-Canyon Meadow Course

Address: 13410 West Morrison Road
Lakewood, CO 80228

Phone #: (303) 986-7888
Tee Times: (303) 986-7888

Tee Time Info: (resident): 7 day advance
(non-resident): 6 day advance

Green Fees: **(resident):** $22.00

(non-resident): $27.00

Credit Cards: Master Card, Visa
Discounts: seniors, juniors

Number of Holes: 18
Number of Courses on Site: 3

	Championship Tees	Men's Tees	Ladies' Tees
Par:	71	71	71
Length:	6808	6562	5203
Course Rating:	71.2	70.0	69.9
Slope:	138	134	121

Year Opened: 1993

Golf Carts Available: yes   **Cart Fee:** $10 per player
Driving Range: yes
On Site Lodging: no

Tournaments: yes

Annual Number of Golf Days: 280
Total Rounds Played Annually: 82,000

General Manager: Craig Parzybok
Head Pro: Craig Parzybok
Superintendent: Don Tolson

Designer/Architect: Denis Griffiths
Average Play Time: 4:10
Special Features: clubhouse, practice green, chipping green

Haystack Mountain Golf Course

Address: 5877 Niwot Road
P.O. Box 636
Longmont, CO 80501
Phone #: (303) 530-1400
Tee Times: (303) 530-1400

Tee Time Info: (resident): advance tee times not available
(non-resident): advance tee times not available

Green Fees: **(resident):** $13.00 weekday
$14.00 weekend
(non-resident): $13.00 weekday
$14.00 weekend
Credit Cards: Master Card, Visa
Discounts: seniors

Number of Holes: 9
Number of Courses on Site: 1

	Championship Tees	Men's Tees	Ladies' Tees
Par:	no	64	64
Length:	no	3900	3772
Course Rating:	no	57.9	59.3
Slope:	no	87	85

Year Opened: 1965

Golf Carts Available: only pull   **Cart Fee:** $3.00
Driving Range: yes
On Site Lodging: no

Tournaments: yes

Annual Number of Golf Days: 360
Total Rounds Played Annually: 41,000

General Manager: Helen Johns
Head Pro: no
Superintendent: J. Clay Johns

Designer/Architect: C.J. Ebel, Jr.
Average Play Time: 2:15
Special Features: club rental, pro shop, snack bar

Heather Gardens Country Club

Address: 2888 South Heather Gardens Way
Aurora, CO 80014

Phone #: (303) 751-2390
Tee Times: (303) 751-2390

Tee Time Info: **(resident):** priority (members)
(non-resident): 5 day advance

Green Fees: **(resident):** $4.00 (members)
$7.00 (guests)
(non-resident): $9.00

Credit Cards: Master Card, Visa
Discounts: no

Number of Holes: 9
Number of Courses on Site: 1

	Championship Tees	Men's Tees	Ladies' Tees
Par:	REVISING	COURSE	DUE
Length:		TO	
Course Rating:		RENOVATION	
Slope:			

Year Opened: 1974

Golf Carts Available: yes   **Cart Fee:** $8.00
Driving Range: yes
On Site Lodging: no

Annual Number of Golf Days: 300
Total Rounds Played Annually: 42,500

General Manager: Robert Macaluso
Head Pro: Robert Macaluso
Superintendent: Todd Jeffers

Average Play Time: 3:15
Special Features: pro shop, restaurant

Hyland Hills - Gold Course

Address: 9650 North Sheridan Boulevard
Westminster, CO 80030

Phone #: (303) 428-6526
Tee Times: (303) 428-6526

Tee Time Info: (resident): 1 day advance (weekdays), Wed. & Fri. (ends)
(non-resident): 1 day advance (weekdays), Wed. & Fri. (ends)

Green Fees: **(resident):** $14.00

(non-resident): $19.00

Credit Cards: Master Card, Visa, American Express
Discounts: no

Number of Holes: 18
Number of Courses on Site: 4

	Championship Tees	Men's Tees	Ladies' Tees
Par:	72	72	73
Length:	7021	6693	5654
Course Rating:	71.9	70.2	71.9
Slope:	132	127	120

Year Opened: 1985

Golf Carts Available: yes   **Cart Fee:** $17.55
Driving Range: yes
On Site Lodging: no

Tournaments: yes

Annual Number of Golf Days: 320
Total Rounds Played Annually: 49,942

General Manager: Todd Thibault
Head Pro: Marv Mazone
Superintendent: Kreg Renzelman

Designer/Architect: Frank Hummel
Average Play Time: 3:49
Special Features: one of America's top 75 public courses, <u>Golf Digest</u>

Hyland Hills - Blue Course

Address: 9650 North Sheridan Boulevard
Westminster, CO 80030

Phone #:   (303) 428-6526
Tee Times: (303) 428-6526

Tee Time Info: (resident):   1 day advance (weekdays), Wed. & Fri. (ends)
                 (non-resident): 1 day advance (weekdays), Wed. & Fri. (ends)

Green Fees: **(resident):** $14.00

                (non-resident): $19.00

Credit Cards: Master Card, Visa, American Express
Discounts: no

Number of Holes: 18
Number of Courses on Site: 4

	Championship Tees	Men's Tees	Ladies' Tees
Par:	74	74	74
Length:	6996	6572	6194
Course Rating:	no rating	68.7	no rating
Slope:	120	115	112

Year Opened: 1963

Golf Carts Available: yes   **Cart Fee:** $17.55
Driving Range: yes
On Site Lodging: no

Annual Number of Golf Days: 320
Total Rounds Played Annually: 61,576

General Manager: Todd Thibault
Head Pro: Marv Mazone
Superintendent: Kreg Renzelman

Designer/Architect: Henry Hughes
Average Play Time: 3:51
Special Features: restaurant, racquetball, lighted practice range

Indian Peaks Golf Course

Address: 2300 Indian Peaks Trail
Lafayette, CO 80026

Phone #: (303) 666-4706
Tee Times: (303) 666-4706

Tee Time Info: (resident): 1 day advance (weekdays), 5 1/2 (weekends)
(non-resident): 1 day advance (weekdays), 5 1/2 (weekends)

Green Fees: **(resident):** $17.00 weekday
$ 25.00 weekend
(non-resident): $27.00

Credit Cards: Master Card, Visa
Discounts: no

Number of Holes: 18
Number of Courses on Site: 1

	Championship Tees	Men's Tees	Ladies' Tees
Par:	72	72	72
Length:	7083	6617	6000
Course Rating:	72.5	70.4	72.5
Slope:	134	123	122

Year Opened: 1993

Golf Carts Available: yes   **Cart Fee:** $20.00
Driving Range: yes
On Site Lodging: no

Tournaments: yes

Annual Number of Golf Days: 277
Total Rounds Played Annually: 45,000

General Manager: no
Head Pro: Craig Stephens
Superintendent: Monte Stevenson

Designer/Architect: Hale Irwin
Average Play Time: 3:51
Special Features: clubhouse

Indian Tree Golf Course

Address: 7555 Wadsworth Boulevard
Arvada, CO 80005

Phone #: (303) 423-3450
Tee Times: (303) 420-1818

Tee Time Info: (resident): 3 day advance
(non-resident): 1 day advance

Green Fees: (resident): $15.00

(non-resident): $18.00

Credit Cards: Master Card, Visa
Discounts: no

Number of Holes: 18
Number of Courses on Site: 1

	Championship Tees	Men's Tees	Ladies' Tees
Par:	70	70	75
Length:	6742	6339	5850
Course Rating:	69.6	67.9	71.2
Slope:	114	108	117

Year Opened: 1971

Golf Carts Available: yes   **Cart Fee:** $18.00
Driving Range: yes
On Site Lodging: no

Tournaments: yes

Annual Number of Golf Days: 315
Total Rounds Played Annually: 96,388

General Manager: Vic Kline
Head Pro: Vic Kline
Superintendent: Jim Gerstner

Designer/Architect: Phelps - Bauer
Average Play Time: 3:46
Special Features: clubhouse, putting range, bar, restaurant, pro shop

Inverness Golf Club

Address: 200 Inverness Drive West
Englewood, CO 80112

Phone #:   (303) 799-9660
Tee Times: (303) 799-9660

Tee Time Info: (resident):   3 day advance (members & resort guests)
(non-resident):   not available

Green Fees: (resident): $65.00 (resort guests)

(non-resident):   membership or hotel stay required

Credit Cards: all major
Discounts: twilight, memberships

Number of Holes: 18
Number of Courses on Site: 1

	Championship Tees	Men's Tees	Ladies' Tees
Par:	70	70	71
Length:	6948	6407	5681
Course Rating:	71.2	68.9	72.6
Slope:	127	125	126

Year Opened: 1974

Golf Carts Available: yes   **Cart Fee:** $12 per player
Driving Range: yes
On Site Lodging: yes

Tournaments: yes

Annual Number of Golf Days: 300
Total Rounds Played Annually: 33,000 - 40,000

General Manager: Mark Hickey
Head Pro: Bob Stallman
Superintendent: Rollie Cahalane

Designer/Architect: Press Maxwell
Average Play Time: 4:04
Special Features: Scanticon Denver Hotel/Resort/Conference Center

John F. Kennedy - East Creek Course

Address: 10500 East Hampden Avenue
Aurora, CO 80014

Phone #: (303) 755-0105
Tee Times: (303) 784-4000

Tee Time Info: (resident): 5 day advance
(non-resident): 3 day advance

Green Fees: (resident): $14.50

(non-resident): $18.75 weekday
$19.75 weekend

Credit Cards: no
Discounts: Denver residents

Number of Holes: 9
Number of Courses on Site: 3

	Championship Tees	Men's Tees	Ladies' Tees
Par:	71	71	72
Length:	6868	6481	5729
Course Rating:	71.6	69.8	69.8
Slope:	131	120	121

Year Opened: 1994

Golf Carts Available: yes   **Cart Fee:** $20.00
Driving Range: yes
On Site Lodging: no

Tournaments: yes

Annual Number of Golf Days: 300
Total Rounds Played Annually: 120,000

General Manager: no
Head Pro: Stacey Hart
Superintendent: Gary Wood

Designer/Architect: Henry Hubbles
Average Play Time: 4:15
Special Features: restaurant, arcade mini-golf, par 3 course

John F. Kennedy-West Creek Course

Address: 10500 East Hampden Avenue
Aurora, CO 80014

Phone #: (303) 755-0105
Tee Times: (303) 784-4000

Tee Time Info: (resident): 5 day advance
(non-resident): 3 day advance

Green Fees: (resident): $14.50

(non-resident): $18.75 weekday
$19.75 weekend

Credit Cards: no
Discounts: yes

Number of Holes: 9
Number of Courses on Site: 3

	Championship Tees	Men's Tees	Ladies' Tees
Par:	71	71	74
Length:	6753	6373	5729
Course Rating:	70.9	69.1	68.9
Slope:	124	115	115

Year Opened: 1994

Golf Carts Available: yes **Cart Fee:** $20.00
Driving Range: yes
On Site Lodging: no

Tournaments: yes

Annual Number of Golf Days: 300
Total Rounds Played Annually: 120,000

General Manager: no
Head Pro: Stacey Hart
Superintendent: Gary Wood

Designer/Architect: Henry Hubbles
Average Play Time: 3:51
Special Features: restaurant, arcade, mini-golf, par 3 course

John F. Kennedy - West/East Course

Address: 10500 East Hampden Avenue
Aurora, CO 80014

Phone #: (303) 755-0105
Tee Times: (303) 784-4000

Tee Time Info: **(resident):** 5 day advance
(non-resident): 3 day advance

Green Fees: **(resident):** $14.50

(non-resident): $18.75 weekday
$19.75 weekend

Credit Cards: no
Discounts: yes

Number of Holes: 9
Number of Courses on Site: 3

	Championship Tees	Men's Tees	Ladies' Tees
Par:	72	72	76
Length:	7009	6756	6416
Course Rating:	71.7	70.6	70.4
Slope:	118	113	115

Year Opened: 1965

Golf Carts Available: yes **Cart Fee:** $20.00
Driving Range: yes
On Site Lodging: no

Tournaments: yes

Annual Number of Golf Days: 300
Total Rounds Played Annually: 120,000

General Manager: no
Head Pro: Stacey Hart
Superintendent: Gary Wood

Designer/Architect: Henry Hubbles
Average Play Time: 3:54
Special Features: restaurant, arcade, mini-golf, par 3 course

Lake Arbor Golf Course

Address: 8600 Wadsworth Boulevard
Arvada, CO 80003

Phone #: (303) 423-1643
Tee Times: (303) 423-1650

Tee Time Info: (resident): 1 day advance
(non-resident): 1 day advance

Green Fees: (resident): $11.50

(non-resident): $15.50

Credit Cards: Master Card, Visa
Discounts: no

Number of Holes: 18
Number of Courses on Site: 1

	Championship Tees	Men's Tees	Ladies' Tees
Par:	70	70	69
Length:	5865	5655	4965
Course Rating:	66.7	65.7	71.1
Slope:	111	108	113

Year Opened: 1973

Golf Carts Available: yes   **Cart Fee:** $17.00
Driving Range: yes
On Site Lodging: no

Tournaments: yes

Annual Number of Golf Days: 300
Total Rounds Played Annually: 65,377

General Manager: no
Head Pro: Jay Ewing
Superintendent: Steve Lynes

Designer/Architect: Noble Caalfant
Average Play Time: 3:29
Special Features: restaurant, bar, pro shop

Lake Valley Golf Club

Address: 4400 Lake Valley Drive
Longmont, CO 80503

Phone #: (303) 444-2114
Tee Times: (303) 444-2114

Tee Time Info: **(resident):** 3 day advance
(non-resident): 3 day advance

Green Fees: **(resident):** $18.00 weekday
$23.00 weekend
(non-resident): $18.00 weekday
$23.00 weekend
Credit Cards: Master Card, Visa
Discounts: twilight, low season

Number of Holes: 18
Number of Courses on Site: 1

	Championship Tees	Men's Tees	Ladies' Tees
Par:	70	70	70
Length:	6725	6273	5713
Course Rating:	69.6	67.8	71.8
Slope:	121	118	119

Year Opened: 1964

Golf Carts Available: yes **Cart Fee:** $19.00
Driving Range: yes
On Site Lodging: no

Tournaments: yes

Annual Number of Golf Days: 240
Total Rounds Played Annually: 50,000

General Manager: Mitchell Galnick
Head Pro: Jim Phillips
Superintendent: Gary Epperson

Designer/Architect: Press Maxwell
Average Play Time: 3:36
Special Features: practice facility, chipping green, putting green

Legacy Ridge Golf Course

Address: 10801 Legacy Ridge Parkway
Westminster, CO 80030

Phone #: (303) 438-8997
Tee Times: (303) 430-2400

Tee Time Info: (resident): advance tee times not available
(non-resident): advance tee times not available

Green Fees: **(resident):** $17.00 weekday
$21.00 weekend
(non-resident): $23.00 weekday
$27.00 weekend
Credit Cards: Master Card, Visa
Discounts: seniors, juniors

Number of Holes: 18
Number of Courses on Site: 1

	Championship Tees	Men's Tees	Ladies' Tees
Par:	72	72	72
Length:	7251	6765	6073
Course Rating:	74.0	71.7	74.5
Slope:	134	127	132

Year Opened: 1994

Golf Carts Available: yes   **Cart Fee:** $18.00
Driving Range: yes
On Site Lodging: no

Tournaments: yes

Annual Number of Golf Days: 300
Total Rounds Played Annually: 45,000

General Manager: no
Head Pro: Ray Fielder
Superintendent: Scott Tuggle

Designer/Architect: Arthur Hills
Average Play Time: 4:00
Special Features: 10,000 square foot full-service clubhouse

Link - N - Greens - North Course

Address: 777 East Lincoln Avenue
Fort Collins, CO 80524

Phone #:   (970) 221-4818
Tee Times: (970) 221-4818

Tee Time Info: (resident):   2 day advance
(non-resident):   2 day advance

Green Fees: **(resident):** $14.00 weekday
$15.00 weekend
(non-resident): $14.00 weekday
$15.00 weekend
Credit Cards: Master Card, Visa
Discounts: seniors, juniors

Number of Holes: 9
Number of Courses on Site: 2

	Championship Tees	Men's Tees	Ladies' Tees
Par:	Not Available At Press	Not Available At Press	Not Available At Press
Length:	Not Available At Press	4814	4530
Course Rating:	Not Available At Press	60.8	59.7
Slope:	Not Available At Press	89	85

Year Opened: 1986

Golf Carts Available: yes   **Cart Fee:** $17.00
Driving Range: yes
On Site Lodging: no

Tournaments: no

Annual Number of Golf Days: 280
Total Rounds Played Annually: 36,000

General Manager: Mike Musgrave
Head Pro: Mike Musgrave
Superintendent: Randy Beard

Designer/Architect: C.A. Musgrave
Average Play Time: 3:07
Special Features: pro shop

Link - N - Greens - South Course

Address: 777 East Lincoln Avenue
Fort Collins, CO 80524

Phone #: (970) 221-4818
Tee Times: (970) 221-4818

Tee Time Info: (resident): 2 day advance
(non-resident): 2 day advance

Green Fees: **(resident):** $14.00 weekday
$15.00 weekend
(non-resident): $14.00 weekday
$15.00 weekend
Credit Cards: Master Card, Visa
Discounts: seniors, juniors

Number of Holes: 9
Number of Courses on Site: 2

	Championship Tees	Men's Tees	Ladies' Tees
Par:	Not Available At Press	Not Available At Press	Not Available At Press
Length:	Not Available At Press	4980	4790
Course Rating:	Not Available At Press	62.3	61.5
Slope:	Not Available At Press	96	94

Year Opened: 1986

Golf Carts Available: yes   **Cart Fee:** $15.00
Driving Range: yes
On Site Lodging: no

Tournaments: no

Annual Number of Golf Days: 280
Total Rounds Played Annually: 36,000

General Manager: Mike Musgrave
Head Pro: Mike Musgrave
Superintendent: Randy Beard

Designer/Architect: C.A. Musgrave
Average Play Time: 3:18
Special Features: pro shop

The Links at Highland's Ranch

Address: 5815 East Gleneagles Village Parkway
Highlands Ranch, CO 80126

Phone #: (303) 470-9292
Tee Times: (303) 470-9292

Tee Time Info: (resident): 5 day advance
(non-resident): 5 day advance

Green Fees: **(resident):** $16.00 weekday
$17.00 weekend
(non-resident): $19.00 weekday
$20.00 weekend
Credit Cards: Master Card, Visa, Discover
Discounts: seniors, juniors

Number of Holes: 18
Number of Courses on Site: 1

	Championship Tees	Men's Tees	Ladies' Tees
Par:	72	72	72
Length:	4576	3992	3337
Course Rating:	Not Available At Press	58.1	59.2
Slope:	Not Available At Press	91	88

Year Opened: 1985

Golf Carts Available: yes   **Cart Fee:** $20.00
Driving Range: yes
On Site Lodging: no

Tournaments: yes

Annual Number of Golf Days: 310
Total Rounds Played Annually: 54,000

General Manager: Sandy Loeffler
Head Pro: Bill Loeffler
Superintendent: Jeff Clouthier

Designer/Architect: Dick Phelps
Average Play Time: 3:13
Special Features: clubhouse, grill

Lone Tree Country Club Golf Course

Address: 9808 Sunningdale Boulevard
Littleton, CO 80124

Phone #: (303) 799-9940
Tee Times: (303) 799-9940

Tee Time Info: (resident): 1 day advance (weekdays), 5 1/2 (weekends)
(non-resident): 1 day advance (weekdays), 2-3 (weekends)

Green Fees: (resident): $18.00 weekday
$32.00 weekend
(non-resident): $25.00 weekday
$45.00 weekend
Credit Cards: Master Card, Visa, American Express, Discover
Discounts: no

Number of Holes: 18
Number of Courses on Site: 1

	Championship Tees	Men's Tees	Ladies' Tees
Par:	72	72	72
Length:	7012	6468	6033
Course Rating:	72.1	69.4	74.5
Slope:	127	121	128

Year Opened: 1985

Golf Carts Available: yes
Driving Range: yes
On Site Lodging: yes

Cart Fee: $10 per player

Tournaments: yes

Annual Number of Golf Days: 260
Total Rounds Played Annually: 25,600

General Manager: South Suburban Metro Rec. and Park District
Head Pro: Bill Ramsey

Designer/Architect: Arnold Palmer - Ed Seay
Average Play Time: 4:08
Special Features: 55,000 square foot clubhouse

Loveland Municipal Golf Course

Address: 2115 West 29th Street
Loveland, CO 80538

Phone #: (970) 667-5256
Tee Times: (970) 669-5800

Tee Time Info: (resident): 5 day advance
(non-resident): 5 day advance

Green Fees: (resident): $16.00 weekday
$18.00 weekend
(non-resident): $16.00 weekday
$18.00 weekend

Credit Cards: Master Card, Visa
Discounts: no

Number of Holes: 18
Number of Courses on Site: 1

	Championship Tees	Men's Tees	Ladies' Tees
Par:	72	72	72
Length:	6827	6425	5498
Course Rating:	69.9	68.4	70.6
Slope:	120	116	117

Year Opened: 1960

Golf Carts Available: yes   **Cart Fee:** $20.00
Driving Range: yes
On Site Lodging: no

Tournaments: yes

Annual Number of Golf Days: 295
Total Rounds Played Annually: 68,300

General Manager: Rod Chapman
Head Pro: Mike Sloan
Superintendent: David Cumpsten

Designer/Architect: Henry Hughes, Dick Phelps
Average Play Time: 3:51
Special Features: clubhouse, pro shop

Mariana Butte Golf Course

Address: 701 Club House Drive
Loveland, CO 80537

Phone #: (970) 667-8308
Tee Times: (970) 669-5800

Tee Time Info: (resident): 5 day advance
(non-resident): 5 day advance

Green Fees: (resident): $12.00 weekday
$15.00 weekend
(non-resident): $18.00 weekday
$25.00 weekend
Credit Cards: Master Card, Visa
Discounts: twilight

Number of Holes: 18
Number of Courses on Site: 1

	Championship Tees	Men's Tees	Ladies' Tees
Par:	72	72	72
Length:	6572	5956	5420
Course Rating:	70.6	67.1	70.2
Slope:	130	116	121

Year Opened: 1992

Golf Carts Available: yes **Cart Fee:** $20.00
Driving Range: yes
On Site Lodging: no

Tournaments: yes

Annual Number of Golf Days: 280
Total Rounds Played Annually: 46,000

General Manager: Rod Chapman
Head Pro: Kent Heusinkveld
Superintendent: Ron Mielke

Designer/Architect: Dick Phelps
Average Play Time: 3:41
Special Features: 5th best new public golf course in 1993, <u>Golf Digest</u>

Meadow Hills Golf Course

Address: 3609 South Dawson Street
Aurora, CO 80014

Phone #: (303) 690-2500
Tee Times: (303) 397-1818

Tee Time Info: (resident): 5 day advance
(non-resident): 3 day advance

Green Fees: (resident): $15.00 weekday
$16.00 weekend
(non-resident): $22.00 weekday
$24.00 weekend
Credit Cards: Master Card, Visa
Discounts: twilight

Number of Holes: 18
Number of Courses on Site: 1

	Championship Tees	Men's Tees	Ladies' Tees
Par:	70	70	71
Length:	6492	6122	5404
Course Rating:	70.6	68.9	74.0
Slope:	134	131	128

Year Opened: 1957

Golf Carts Available: yes   **Cart Fee:** $18.00
Driving Range: yes
On Site Lodging: no

Tournaments: yes

Annual Number of Golf Days: 300
Total Rounds Played Annually: 65,000

General Manager: Tom Farrell
Head Pro: Mickey Byrne
Superintendent: Tom Farrell

Designer/Architect: Henry Hughes
Average Play Time: 3:50
Special Features: restaurant, swimming pool, tennis, pro shop

The Meadows Golf Club

Address: 6937 South Simms Street
Littleton, CO 80127

Phone #:   (303) 972-8831
Tee Times: (303) 972-8831

Tee Time Info: (resident):   3 day advance
                 (non-resident): 2 day advance

Green Fees: **(resident):** $14.25

                (non-resident): $21.50

Credit Cards: Master Card, Visa
Discounts: no

Number of Holes: 18
Number of Courses on Site: 1

	Championship Tees	Men's Tees	Ladies' Tees
Par:	72	72	72
Length:	6995	6565	5416
Course Rating:	71.6	69.6	71.1
Slope:	130	125	123

Year Opened: 1983

Golf Carts Available: yes   **Cart Fee:** $20.00
Driving Range: yes
On Site Lodging: no

Tournaments: yes

Annual Number of Golf Days: 300
Total Rounds Played Annually: 57,534

General Manager: Robert J. Bonacci
Head Pro: Pat Tait
Superintendent: John Fitzgibbons

Designer/Architect: Dick Phelps
Average Play Time: 4:00
Special Features: restaurant, banquet facility, clubhouse

Mira Vista Golf Course

Address: 10110 E. Golfers Way
Aurora, CO 80010

Phone #: (303) 340-1520
Tee Times: (303) 397-1818

Tee Time Info: (resident): 5 day advance
(non-resident): 3 day advance

Green Fees: (resident): $16.00

(non-resident): $19.00

Credit Cards: Master Card, Visa
Discounts: seniors, juniors

Number of Holes: 18
Number of Courses on Site: 1

	Championship Tees	Men's Tees	Ladie's Tees
Par:	72	72	72
Length:	6830	6474	5919
Course Rating:	71.2	69.7	72.6
Slope:	127	122	120

Year Opened: 1994 (formerly Lowry Air Force Base Golf Course)

Golf Carts Available: yes   **Cart Fee:** $18.00
Driving Range: yes
On Site Lodging: no

Tournaments: yes

Annual Number of Golf Days: 300
Total Rounds Played Annually: 60,000

General Manager: Don Chelemedos
Head Pro: Don Chelemedos
Superintendent: Dave Nadol

Average Play Time: 4:15
Special Features: proshop, Mira Vista Grill, 5,000 sq. ft. clubhouse

Mountain View Golf Course

Address: 5091 South Quebec Street
Denver, CO 80237

Phone #: (303) 694-3012
Tee Times: (303) 694-3102

Tee Time Info: (resident): 1 day advance (weekdays), Wed. (weekends)
(non-resident): 1 day advance (weekdays), Wed. (weekends)

Green Fees: (resident): $12.00

(non-resident): $12.00

Credit Cards: no
Discounts: no

Number of Holes: 9
Number of Courses on Site: 1

	Championship Tees	Men's Tees	Ladies' Tees
Par:	no	66	64
Length:	no	5012	4176
Course Rating:	no	63.7	66.1
Slope:	no	102	101

Year Opened: 1984

Golf Carts Available: yes   **Cart Fee:** $12.00
Driving Range: yes
On Site Lodging: yes

Tournaments: yes

Annual Number of Golf Days: 320
Total Rounds Played Annually: 25,000

General Manager: Ralph Haddad
Head Pro: Ralph Haddad
Superintendent: Joe Stoudt

Designer/Architect: Ralph Haddad
Average Play Time: 3:09
Special Features: mini-golf, pro shop, night range, restaurant

Mountain Vista Greens Ltd.

Address: 2808 Northeast Frontage Road
Fort Collins, CO 80524

Phone #:   (970) 482-4847
Tee Times: (970) 482-4847

Tee Time Info: (resident): 7 day advance
(non-resident): 7 day advance

Green Fees: **(resident):** $9.00

(non-resident): $9.00

Credit Cards: Master Card, Visa
Discounts: seniors, juniors

Number of Holes: 9
Number of Courses on Site: 1

	Championship Tees	Men's Tees	Ladies' Tees
Par:	36	36	36
Length:	3494	3198	2731
Course Rating:	36.0	34.4	33.8
Slope:	123	123	102

Year Opened: 1992

Golf Carts Available: yes   **Cart Fee:** $12.00
Driving Range: yes
On Site Lodging: no

Tournaments: yes

Annual Number of Golf Days: 280

General Manager: Jeanne Matsuda
Head Pro: Harold Garrison, Pat Johnson
Superintendent: Bob Ramsey

Designer/Architect: Victor Tawara
Average Play Time: 4:00
Special Features: pro shop, putting greens

Overland Golf Course

Address: 1801 South Huron Street
Denver, CO 80223

Phone #: (303) 777-7331
Tee Times: (303) 784-4000

Tee Time Info: (resident): 5 day advance
(non-resident): 3 day advance

Green Fees: **(resident):** $13.50 weekday
$14.50 weekend
(non-resident): $18.75 weekday
$19.75 weekend
Credit Cards: Master Card, Visa
Discounts: no

Number of Holes: 18
Number of Courses on Site: 1

	Championship Tees	Men's Tees	Ladies' Tees
Par:	no	72	74
Length:	no	6312	6126
Course Rating:	no	69.2	72.7
Slope:	no	114	115

Year Opened: 1895, 1952

Golf Carts Available: yes **Cart Fee:** $18.00
Driving Range: yes
On Site Lodging: no

Tournaments: yes

Annual Number of Golf Days: 300
Total Rounds Played Annually: 81,000

General Manager: Ron Reif
Head Pro: Ron Rief
Superintendent: Gary Boyd

Designer/Architect: Henry Walcott
Average Play Time: 3:47
Special Features: bar, restaurant, lessons, pro shop

Park Hill Golf Club

Address: 4141 East 35th Avenue
Denver, CO 80207

Phone #: (303) 333-5411
Tee Times: (303) 333-5411

Tee Time Info: (resident): 6 day advance
(non-resident): 6 day advance

Green Fees: (resident): $19.00 weekday
$22.00 weekend
(non-resident): $19.00 weekday
$22.00 weekend

Credit Cards: Master Card, Visa
Discounts: no

Number of Holes: 18
Number of Courses on Site: 1

	Championship Tees	Men's Tees	Ladies' Tees
Par:	71	71	72
Length:	6585	6396	6396
Course Rating:	69.4	69.4	73.4
Slope:	120	120	124

Year Opened: 1930

Golf Carts Available: yes   **Cart Fee:** $22.00
Driving Range: yes
On Site Lodging: no

Tournaments: yes

Annual Number of Golf Days: 300

General Manager: Dutch Claussen, Kim Boucher
Head Pro: Kevin Fonk
Superintendent: Kim Boucher

Designer/Architect: Clark Hamilton
Average Play Time: 3:45
Special Features: full clubhouse with restaurant, pro shop

Ptarmigan Golf and Country Club

Address: 5410 Vardon Way
Fort Collins, CO 80525

Phone #: (970) 226-6600
Tee Times: (970) 226-6600

Tee Time Info: (resident): first priority (members)
(non-resident): 2 day advance (weekdays), Th. (weekends)

Green Fees: **(resident):** memberships

(non-resident): $25.00 weekday
$40.00 Fri. w/ cart, $50.00 Sat. & Sun. w/ cart
Credit Cards: Master Card, Visa
Discounts: no

Number of Holes: 18
Number of Courses on Site: 1

	Championship Tees	Men's Tees	Ladies' Tees
Par:	72	72	72
Length:	7201	6586	5658
Course Rating:	73.0	70.0	70.9
Slope:	135	128	116

Year Opened: 1988

Golf Carts Available: yes   **Cart Fee:** $20.00
Driving Range: yes
On Site Lodging: no

Tournaments: yes

Annual Number of Golf Days: 260
Total Rounds Played Annually: 30,000

General Manager: Hersh McGraw
Head Pro: Jim Eyberg
Superintendent: Scott Robbins

Designer/Architect: Jack Nicklaus Co.
Average Play Time: 4:09
Special Features: two lighted tennis courts, swimming pool, pro shop

Raccoon Creek Golf Course

Address: 7301 West Bowles Avenue
Littleton, CO 80123

Phone #: (303) 973-9684
Tee Times: (303) 973-4653

Tee Time Info: (resident): 2 day advance
(non-resident): 2 day advance

Green Fees: (resident): $26.00

(non-resident): $26.00

Credit Cards: Master Card, Visa, Discover
Discounts: seniors, juniors, Mondays, Tuesdays

Number of Holes: 18
Number of Courses on Site: 1

	Championship Tees	Men's Tees	Ladies' Tees
Par:	72	72	72
Length:	7045	6517	6517
Course Rating:	72.5	70.1	76.1
Slope:	133	126	134

Year Opened: 1983

Golf Carts Available: yes   **Cart Fee:** $20.00
Driving Range: yes
On Site Lodging: no

Tournaments: yes

Annual Number of Golf Days: 300
Total Rounds Played Annually: 55,000

General Manager: Jeff Carpenter
Head Pro: Dave Detweiler
Superintendent: Anthony Hartsock

Designer/Architect: Dick Phelps
Average Play Time: 4:07
Special Features: restaurant, clubhouse, pro shop

Riverdale Golf Club - Dunes Course

Address: 13300 Riverdale Road
Brighton, CO 80601

Phone #: (303) 659-6700
Tee Times: (303) 659-6700

Tee Time Info: (resident): 2 day advance (weekdays), 5 1/2 (weekends)
(non-resident): 2 day advance (weekdays), 5 1/2 (weekends)

Green Fees: **(resident):** $23.00 weekday
$26.00 weekend
(non-resident): $26.00

Credit Cards: Master Card, Visa
Discounts: no

Number of Holes: 18
Number of Courses on Site: 2

	Championship Tees	Men's Tees	Ladies' Tees
Par:	72	72	72
Length:	7027	6354	4902
Course Rating:	71.9	68.8	67.5
Slope:	124	118	108

Year Opened: 1986

Golf Carts Available: yes   **Cart Fee:** $19.00
Driving Range: yes
On Site Lodging: no

Tournaments: yes

Annual Number of Golf Days: 285
Total Rounds Played Annually: 88,843

General Manager: Bob Doyle
Head Pro: Bob Lewis
Superintendent: D'Ann Kimbrel

Designer/Architect: Pete Dye, Perry Dye
Average Play Time: 3:59
Special Features: runner-up for Best New Public course of 1986

Riverdale Golf Club - Knolls Course

Address: 13300 Riverdale Road
Brighton, CO 80601

Phone #: (303) 659-6700
Tee Times: (303) 659-6700

Tee Time Info: (resident): 1 day advance (weekdays), 5 1/2 (weekends)
(non-resident): 1 day advance (weekdays), 5 1/2 (weekends)

Green Fees: **(resident):** $23.00 weekday
$26.00 weekend
(non-resident): $26.00

Credit Cards: Master Card, Visa
Discounts: no

Number of Holes: 18
Number of Courses on Site: 2

	Championship Tees	Men's Tees	Ladies' Tees
Par:	71	71	72
Length:	6756	6426	5933
Course Rating:	70.6	68.7	71.8
Slope:	114	111	115

Year Opened: 1986

Golf Carts Available: yes   **Cart Fee:** $20.00
Driving Range: yes
On Site Lodging: no

Tournaments: yes

Annual Number of Golf Days: 285
Total Rounds Played Annually: 88,843

General Manager: Bob Doyle
Head Pro: Bob Lewis

Designer/Architect: Pete Dye, Perry Dye
Average Play Time: 3:56
Special Features: restaurant, banquet room, clubhouse

Southridge Golf Club

Address: 5750 South Lemay Avenue
Fort Collins, CO 80525

Phone #:   (970) 226-2828
Tee Times: (970) 226-2828

Tee Time Info: (resident):   3 day advance
(non-resident): 3 day advance

Green Fees: (resident): $17.00

(non-resident): $17.00

Credit Cards: Master Card, Visa
Discounts: juniors

Number of Holes: 18
Number of Courses on Site: 1

	Championship Tees	Men's Tees	Ladies' Tees
Par:	71	71	71
Length:	6363	5731	5058
Course Rating:	69.1	66.4	69.3
Slope:	122	116	118

Year Opened: 1984

Golf Carts Available: yes   **Cart Fee:** $18.00
Driving Range: yes
On Site Lodging: no

Tournaments: yes

Annual Number of Golf Days: 250
Total Rounds Played Annually: 48,000

General Manager: no
Head Pro: Derek M. Cordova
Superintendent: Randy Bonneville

Designer/Architect: Frank Hummel
Average Play Time: 3:39
Special Features: pro shop, restaurant

South Suburban Golf Course

Address: 7900 South Colorado Boulevard
Littleton, CO 80122

Phone #: (303) 770-5500
Tee Times: (303) 770-5508

Tee Time Info: (resident):   1 day advance (weekdays), 5 1/2 (weekends)
(non-resident): 1 day advance (weekdays), 2-3 (weekends)

Green Fees: **(resident):** $14.00

                (non-resident): $22.50

Credit Cards: Master Card, Visa, American Express, Discover
Discounts: no

Number of Holes: 18
Number of Courses on Site: 2

	Championship Tees	Men's Tees	Ladies' Tees
Par:	72	72	72
Length:	6705	6340	6267
Course Rating:	69.6	68.2	68.2
Slope:	120	117	117

Year Opened: 1973

Golf Carts Available: yes   **Cart Fee:** $20.00
Driving Range: yes
On Site Lodging: no

Tournaments: yes

Annual Number of Golf Days: 364
Total Rounds Played Annually: 90,160

General Manager: South Suburban Metropolitan Rec. & Park District
Head Pro: Tom Woodard
Superintendent: Dave Krause

Designer/Architect: Dick Phelps
Average Play Time: 3:48
Special Features: clubhouse, chipping green, par 3 course

Springhill Golf Course

Address: 800 Telluride Street
                  Aurora, CO 80011

Phone #:   (303) 343-3963
Tee Times: (303) 397-1818

Tee Time Info: (resident):   5 day advance
               (non-resident): 3 day advance

Green Fees: **(resident):** $12.00 weekday
                                 $13.00 weekend
            (non-resident): $16.00 weekday
                                 $18.00 weekend
Credit Cards: Master Card, Visa
Discounts: seniors, juniors, twilight

Number of Holes: 18
Number of Courses on Site: 1

	Championship Tees	Men's Tees	Ladies' Tees
Par:	no	64	65
Length:	no	5001	4651
Course Rating:	no	62.1	no rating
Slope:	no	93	93

Year Opened: 1972

Golf Carts Available: yes   **Cart Fee:** $16.00
Driving Range: yes
On Site Lodging: no

Tournaments: yes

Annual Number of Golf Days: 300
Total Rounds Played Annually: 56,000

General Manager: Mickey Byrne
Head Pro: Andy Peterson
Superintendent: Barry Dunbar

Designer/Architect: Dick Phelps
Average Play Time: 3:16
Special Features: snack bar, chipping green, putting green, pro shop

Sunset Golf Course

Address: 1900 Longs Peak Avenue
Longmont, CO 80501

Phone #: (303) 776-3122
Tee Times: (303) 776-3122

Tee Time Info: (resident): 2 day advance
(non-resident): 2 day advance

Green Fees: **(resident):** $8.00 weekday
$9.00 weekend
(non-resident): $10.00 weekday
$11.00 weekend

Credit Cards: no
Discounts: seniors, juniors

Number of Holes: 9
Number of Courses on Site: 1

	Championship Tees	Men's Tees	Ladies' Tees
Par:	68	68	72
Length:	5678	5950	5308
Course Rating:	66.9	65.4	69.3
Slope:	114	111	106

Year Opened: 1923

Golf Carts Available: yes   **Cart Fee:** $18.00
Driving Range: no
On Site Lodging: no

Tournaments: yes

Annual Number of Golf Days: 300
Total Rounds Played Annually: 42,000

General Manager: Peter Bain
Head Pro: Peter Bain
Superintendent: Jeff Weed

Average Play Time: 3:29
Special Features: pro shop, restaurant

Thorncreek Golf Club

Address: 13555 North Washington Street
Thornton, CO 80241

Phone #:   (303) 450-7055
Tee Times: (303) 450-7055

Tee Time Info: (resident):   7 day advance (weekdays), Wed. (weekends)
                 (non-resident): 7 day advance (weekdays), Wed. (weekends)

Green Fees: **(resident):** $15.00 weekday
                            $17.00 weekend
          (non-resident): $26.00

Credit Cards: Master Card, Visa, American Express
Discounts: twilight

Number of Holes: 18
Number of Courses on Site: 1

	Championship Tees	Men's Tees	Ladies' Tees
Par:	72	72	72
Length:	7268	6698	5547
Course Rating:	73.7	71.9	70.5
Slope:	136	131	120

Year Opened: 1992

Golf Carts Available: yes   **Cart Fee:** $10 per player
Driving Range: yes
On Site Lodging: no

Tournaments: yes

Annual Number of Golf Days: 300
Total Rounds Played Annually: 45,000

General Manager: Gregory Fields
Head Pro: Gregory Fields
Superintendent: Ron Conard

Designer/Architect: Baxter, Dye, Spann
Average Play Time: 4:14
Special Features: grill, rental clubs, clubhouse, restaurant

Twin Peaks Golf Course

Address: 1200 Cornell Drive
Longmont, CO 80503

Phone #: (303) 772-1722
Tee Times: (303) 772-1722

Tee Time Info: (resident): 2 day advance
(non-resident): 2 day advance

Green Fees: (resident): $14.00

(non-resident): $16.00

Credit Cards: no
Discounts: no

Number of Holes: 18
Number of Courses on Site: 1

	Championship Tees	Men's Tees	Ladies' Tees
Par:	70	70	71
Length:	6767	6260	5831
Course Rating:	71.3	68.8	71.7
Slope:	120	115	122

Year Opened: 1977

Golf Carts Available: yes   **Cart Fee:** $18.00
Driving Range: yes
On Site Lodging: no

Tournaments: yes

Annual Number of Golf Days: 280
Total Rounds Played Annually: 58,000

General Manager: City of Longmont
Head Pro: Don Corey
Superintendent: Larry Mills

Designer/Architect: Frank Hummel
Average Play Time: 3:56
Special Features: raised, mounded greens, five lakes in play

Wellshire Municipal Golf Course

Address: 3333 South Colorado Boulevard
Denver, CO 80222

Phone #: (303) 757-1352
Tee Times: (303) 784-4000

Tee Time Info: (resident): 5 day advance
(non-resident): 3 day advance

Green Fees: **(resident):** $13.50 weekday
$14.50 weekend
(non-resident): $18.75 weekday
$19.75 weekend

Credit Cards: no
Discounts: no

Number of Holes: 18
Number of Courses on Site: 1

	Championship Tees	Men's Tees	Ladies' Tees
Par:	72	72	77
Length:	6592	6142	5890
Course Rating:	71.1	69.1	72.0
Slope:	117	115	116

Year Opened: 1926

Golf Carts Available: yes   **Cart Fee:** $20.00
Driving Range: yes
On Site Lodging: no

Tournaments: yes

Annual Number of Golf Days: 290
Total Rounds Played Annually: 70,000

General Manager: Scott Hart
Head Pro: Scott Hart
Superintendent: Greg Blew

Designer/Architect: Donald Ross
Average Play Time: 3:44
Special Features: clubhouse, restaurant, pro shop

West Woods Golf Club

Address: 6655 Quaker Street
Golden, CO 80403

Phone #: (303) 424-3334
Tee Times: (303) 424-3334

Tee Time Info: (resident): 1 day advance
(non-resident): 1 day advance

Green Fees: (resident): $22.00

(non-resident): $26.00

Credit Cards: Master Card, Visa
Discounts: no

Number of Holes: 18
Number of Courses on Site: 1

	Championship Tees	Men's Tees	Ladies' Tees
Par:	72	72	74
Length:	7035	6335	5626
Course Rating:	72.1	69.6	71.9
Slope:	135	122	118

Year Opened: 1994

Golf Carts Available: yes   **Cart Fee:** $18.00
Driving Range: yes
On Site Lodging: no

Tournaments: yes

Annual Number of Golf Days: 300
Total Rounds Played Annually: 45,000

General Manager: Richard Dorn
Head Pro: Steve Lynes
Superintendent: Jim Wilkins

Designer/Architect: Dick Phelps
Average Play Time: 4:15
Special Features: rental clubs, practice putting green clubhouse

Willis Case Golf Course

Address: 4999 Vrain Street
Denver, CO 80212

Phone #:   (303) 455-9801
Tee Times: (303) 784-4000

Tee Time Info: (resident):   5 day advance
               (non-resident): 3 day advance

Green Fees: **(resident):** $13.50 weekday
                            $14.50 weekend
           (non-resident): $18.75 weekday
                            $19.75 weekend
Credit Cards: Master Card, Visa
Discounts: no

Number of Holes: 18
Number of Courses on Site: 1

	Championship Tees	Men's Tees	Ladies' Tees
Par:	no	72	75
Length:	no	6364	6144
Course Rating:	no	68.7	72.8
Slope:	no	112	115

Year Opened: 1931

Golf Carts Available: yes   **Cart Fee:** $20.00
Driving Range: no
On Site Lodging: no

Tournaments: yes

Annual Number of Golf Days: 295
Total Rounds Played Annually: 67,972

General Manager: Bernie Hutchinson
Head Pro: Ted Parker
Superintendent: Bernie Hutchinson

Average Play Time: 3:46
Special Features: clubhouse, food, drinks, on-course services

SOUTH CENTRAL REGION

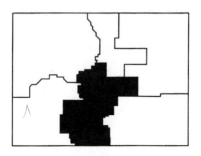

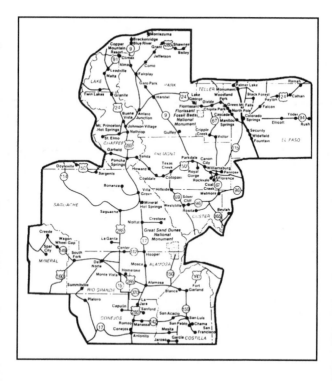

Bear Paw Golf Club

Address: P.O. Box 154
Florence, CO 81226

Phone #: (719) 784-6152
Tee Times: (719) 784-6152

Tee Time Info: (resident): 2 day advance
(non-resident): 2 day advance

Green Fees: **(resident):** $6.50 weekday
$8.00 weekend
(non-resident): $6.50 weekday
$8.00 weekend

Credit Cards: soon
Discounts: no

Number of Holes: 9
Number of Courses on Site: 1

	Championship Tees	Men's Tees	Ladies' Tees
Par:	no	36	36
Length:	no	3124	2657
Course Rating:	no	69.7	no rating
Slope:	no	126	

Year Opened: 1994

Golf Carts Available: yes   **Cart Fee:** $5.50 per player
Driving Range: yes
On Site Lodging: no

Tournaments: yes

Annual Number of Golf Days: opened 1994
Total Rounds Played Annually: opened 1994

General Manager: Arthur Fodor
Head Pro: Arthur Fodor
Superintendent: John Faris

Designer/Architect: Ric Buckton
Average Play Time: 2:06
Special Features: pro shop, snack bar, view of Pikes Peak

The Broadmoor - East Course

Address: Broadmoor Hotel
1 Lake Circle, Box 1439
Colorado Springs, CO 80901
Phone #:   (719) 577-5790, (800) 634-7711
Tee Times: (719) 577-5790, (800) 634-7711

Tee Time Info: (resident):   phone day of play (resort guests & members)
(non-resident): membership or hotel stay required

Green Fees: **(resident):** $83.00 (resort guests & members)

(non-resident):   membership or hotel stay required

Credit Cards: all major
Discounts: no

Number of Holes: 18
Number of Courses on Site: 3

	Championship Tees	Men's Tees	Ladies' Tees
Par:	72	72	72
Length:	7218	6555	5920
Course Rating:	71.4	73.9	74.1
Slope:	122	128	126

Year Opened: 1918

Golf Carts Available: yes   **Cart Fee:** $15 per player
Driving Range: yes
On Site Lodging: yes

Tournaments: yes

Annual Number of Golf Days: 320
Total Rounds Played Annually: 25,000

General Manager: Sherry Watkins
Head Pro: Leo Simontta
Superintendent: Tommy Andersen

Designer/Architect: Donald Ross
Average Play Time: 3:56
Special Features: In America's 75 Best Resort Courses, <u>Golf Digest</u>

The Broadmoor - South Course

Address: Broadmoor Hotel
               1 Lake Circle, Box 1439
               Colorado Springs, CO 80901
Phone #:   (719) 577-5790, (800) 634-7711
Tee Times: (719) 577-5790, (800) 634-7711

Tee Time Info: (resident):   phone day of play (resort guests & members)
                    (non-resident): membership or hotel stay required

Green Fees: **(resident):** $83.00 (resort guests & members)

                 (non-resident): membership or hotel stay required

Credit Cards: all major
Discounts: no

Number of Holes: 18
Number of Courses on Site: 3

	Championship Tees	Men's Tees	Ladies' Tees
Par:	72	72	72
Length:	6781	6108	5609
Course Rating:	72.1	69.4	72.7
Slope:	135	125	129

Year Opened: 1974

Golf Carts Available: yes   **Cart Fee:** $15 per player
Driving Range: yes
On Site Lodging: yes

Tournaments: yes

Annual Number of Golf Days: 320
Total Rounds Played Annually: 25,000

General Manager: Sherry Watkins
Head Pro: Leo Simontta
Superintendent: Tommy Andersen

Designer/Architect: Ed Seay / Arnold Palmer Co.
Average Play Time: 3:53
Special Features: In America's 75 Best Resort Courses, <u>Golf Digest</u>

The Broadmoor - West Course

Address: Broadmoor Hotel
               1 Lake Circle, Box 1439
               Colorado Springs, CO 80901
Phone #:   (719) 577-5790, (800) 634-7711
Tee Times: (719) 577-5790, (800) 634-7711

Tee Time Info: **(resident):**   phone day of play (resort guests & members)
                    (non-resident): membership or hotel stay required

Green Fees: **(resident):** $83.00 (resort guests & members)

                   (non-resident): membership or hotel stay required

Credit Cards: all major
Discounts: no

Number of Holes: 18
Number of Courses on Site: 3

	Championship Tees	Men's Tees	Ladies' Tees
Par:	72	72	73
Length:	6937	6109	5505
Course Rating:	73.4	70.2	71.7
Slope:	134	128	121

Year Opened: 1956

Golf Carts Available: yes   **Cart Fee:** $15 per player
Driving Range: yes
On Site Lodging: yes

Tournaments: yes

Annual Number of Golf Days: 320
Total Rounds Played Annually: 25,000

General Manager: Sherry Watkins
Head Pro: Leo Simontta
Superintendent: Tommy Andersen

Designer/Architect: Robert Trent Jones
Average Play Time: 3:55
Special Features: In America's 75 Best Resort Courses, <u>Golf Digest</u>

Cattalis Golf Club

Address: 6615 North River Road
P.O. Box 1334
Alamosa, CO 81101
Phone #: (719) 589-9515
Tee Times: (719) 589-9515

Tee Time Info: (resident): several days / weeks advance
(non-resident): several days / weeks advance

Green Fees: **(resident):** $18.00

(non-resident): $18.00

Credit Cards: Master Card, Visa
Discounts: seniors, juniors

Number of Holes: 18
Number of Courses on Site: 1

	Championship Tees	Men's Tees	Ladies' Tees
Par:	72	72	73
Length:	6681	6106	5184
Course Rating:	70.0	68.3	69.8
Slope:	129	121	120

Year Opened: 1991

Golf Carts Available: yes **Cart Fee:** $16.00
Driving Range: yes
On Site Lodging: no

Tournaments: yes

Annual Number of Golf Days: 250
Total Rounds Played Annually: 20,000

General Manager: Jack Horner
Head Pro: Lee Maiden
Superintendent: Robbie Jackson

Designer/Architect: Dick Phelps
Average Play Time: 3:53
Special Features: pro shop, clubhouse, natural wetlands

Cimarron Hills Golf Course

Address: 1850 Tuskegee Place
Colorado Springs, CO 80915

Phone #: (719) 597-2637
Tee Times: (719) 597-2637

Tee Time Info: (resident): 7 day advance
(non-resident): 7 day advance

Green Fees: **(resident):** $15.00

(non-resident): $15.00

Credit Cards: no
Discounts: seniors, juniors

Number of Holes: 18
Number of Courses on Site: 2

	Championship Tees	Men's Tees	Ladies' Tees
Par:	no	72	72
Length:	no	6579	5730
Course Rating:	no	68.2	71.4
Slope:	no	117	117

Year Opened: 1972

Golf Carts Available: yes   **Cart Fee:** $16.00
Driving Range: yes
On Site Lodging: no

Tournaments: yes

Annual Number of Golf Days: 313
Total Rounds Played Annually: 43,333

General Manager: Van Russell
Head Pro: no
Superintendent: Troy Boushee

Designer/Architect: Press Maxwell
Average Play Time: 3:49
Special Features: pro shop, club repair

Collegiate Peaks Golf Course

Address: 28775 Fairway Drive
               Buena Vista, CO 81211

Phone #:   (719) 395-8189
Tee Times: (719) 395-8189

Tee Time Info: (resident):   7-14 day advance
              (non-resident): 7-14 day advance

Green Fees: **(resident):** $18.00

               (non-resident): $18.00

Credit Cards: yes
Discounts: no

Number of Holes: 9
Number of Courses on Site: 1

	Championship Tees	Men's Tees	Ladies' Tees
Par:	no	72	72
Length:	no	6161	5442
Course Rating:	no	67.5	67.5
Slope:	no	118	118

Year Opened: 1975

Golf Carts Available: yes   **Cart Fee:** $18.00
Driving Range: yes
On Site Lodging: no

Tournaments: yes

Annual Number of Golf Days: 245
Total Rounds Played Annually: 12,786

General Manager: Skip DiGangi
Head Pro: no
Superintendent: Russ Kaiser

Average Play Time: 3:57
Special Features: clubhouse, pro shop, snack bar

Gleneagle Golf Course

Address: 345 Mission Hills Way
Colorado Springs, CO 80921

Phone #: (719) 488-0900
Tee Times: (719) 488-0900

Tee Time Info: (resident): 3 day advance
(non-resident): 3 day advance

Green Fees: **(resident):** $20.00 weekday
$25.00 weekend
(non-resident): $20.00 weekday
$25.00 weekend
Credit Cards: Master Card, Visa, American Express, Discover
Discounts: low season

Number of Holes: 18
Number of Courses on Site: 1

	Championship Tees	Men's Tees	Ladie's Tees
Par:	72	72	72
Length:	7110	6734	5655
Course Rating:	73.4	71.5	73.2
Slope:	129	126	120

Year Opened: 1972

Golf Carts Available: yes   **Cart Fee:** $20.00
Driving Range: yes
On Site Lodging: no

Tournaments: yes

Annual Number of Golf Days: 320
Total Rounds Played Annually: 28,000

General Manager: Elcio Silva
Head Pro: Scott Lane
Superintendent: Mark Mencin

Designer/Architect: Frank Hummel
Average Play Time: 4:14
Special Features: clubhouse, pro shop, restaurant

Great Sand Dunes C.C. and Inn

Address: 5303 Highway 150
Mosca, CO 81146

Phone #:   (719) 378-2357, (800) 284-9213
Tee Times: (719) 378-2357, (800) 284-9213

Tee Time Info: (resident):   2 week advance (resort guests)
(non-resident): 2 week advance

Green Fees: **(resident):** $65.00 (resort guests)

(non-resident): $65.00

Credit Cards: Master Card, Visa, American Express, Discover
Discounts: no

Number of Holes: 18
Number of Courses on Site: 1

	Championship Tees	Men's Tees	Ladies' Tees
Par:	72	72	72
Length:	7006	6538	5327
Course Rating:	71.2	68.9	67.9
Slope:	120	119	118

Year Opened: 1990, 1994

Golf Carts Available: yes   **Cart Fee:** included
Driving Range: yes
On Site Lodging: yes

Tournaments: no

Annual Number of Golf Days: 160
Total Rounds Played Annually: 5,000

General Manager: Mike Wagner
Head Pro: Mike Wagner
Superintendent: Greg Icabone

Designer/Architect: Sandford & Eweseychik 1990, Dick Phelps 1994
Average Play Time: 3:50
Special Features: bison ranch, Great Sand Dunes National Monument

COMPLETE GUIDE TO PUBLIC GOLF COURSES

GOLF
COLORADO ™

Featuring

143 Public Courses

Locations, Pricing, Tee Times

Tournament Schedule

GOLF

COLORADO ™
Complete Guide To Colorado Public Golf Courses

Global Inc. Worldwide Marketing and Advertising
P.O. Box 2555
Littleton, CO 80161-2555
Phone: (303) 779-1001
Fax: (303) 694-9785

ORDERED BY:

(please print or type legibly)

Name_____

Address_____

City_____

State_____Zip_____

Phone numbers with area codes:

Day(___)_____   Evening(___)_____

Please add $1.55 per book for shipping. Colorado residents please add $.35 per booksales tax.

Quantity	Item Name (Golf Colorado™)	Price Each	Total
		$7 .95	·
		Shipping ($1.55 per book)	·
		CO resident sales tax (.$35 per book)	·
		TOTAL	·

Method of Payment: ☐ check ☐ Master Card ☐ Visa ☐ AmEx.

☐☐☐☐☐☐☐☐☐☐☐☐☐☐☐☐ ☐☐/☐☐

Credit card account number   Expiration Date (mo/yr)

_____   _____

Cardholder's printed name ...   ... and signature

_____

Cardholder's address (if not as above) ...

_____

... City   State   Zip

Los Cumbres Golf Course

Address: 4905 County Road T
P.O. Box 237
Crestone, CO 81131
Phone #: (719) 256-4856, (719) 256-4905
Tee Times: (719) 256-4856

Tee Time Info: (resident): Information not available at time of press

(non-resident): Information not available at time of press

Green Fees: (resident): $9.00

(non-resident): $9.00

Credit Cards: Master Card, Visa
Discounts: yes

Number of Holes: 9
Number of Courses on Site: 1

	Championship Tees	Men's Tees	Ladie's Tees
Par:	31	31	31
Length:	2228	1908	1677
Course Rating:	56.8	56.8	56.8
Slope:	96	89	89

Year Opened: 1974

Golf Carts Available: yes   **Cart Fee:** $2.00 trail fee
Driving Range: yes
On Site Lodging: no

Tournaments: yes

Annual Number of Golf Days: 200
Total Rounds Played Annually: 3,500

General Manager: Neola Lipscomb
Head Pro: no
Superintendent: no

Designer/Architect: Jim Barnes
Average Play Time: 2:56
Special Features: limited lodging and camping facilities avail. in area

Monte Vista Country Club

Address: 101 Country Club Drive
              Monte Vista, CO 81144

Phone #:   (719) 852-4906
Tee Times: (719) 852-4906

Tee Time Info: (resident):   advance tee times not necessary
              (non-resident): advance tee times not necessary

Green Fees: **(resident):** $15.00

              (non-resident): $15.00

Credit Cards: no
Discounts: no

Number of Holes: 9
Number of Courses on Site: 1

	Championship Tees	Men's Tees	Ladies' Tees
Par:	70	70	72
Length:	6088	5950	5122
Course Rating:	67.1	66.6	66.2
Slope:	113	113	113

Year Opened: 1934

Golf Carts Available: yes   **Cart Fee:** $15.00
Driving Range: yes
On Site Lodging: no

Tournaments: yes

Annual Number of Golf Days: 200
Total Rounds Played Annually: 13,000

General Manager: Britt Jardon
Head Pro: no
Superintendent: Britt Jardon

Designer/Architect: James Newman
Average Play Time: 3:39
Special Features: clubhouse, narrow fairways, very small greens

Mount Massive Golf Course

Address: 259 County Road 5
P.O. Box 312
Leadville, CO 80461
Phone #: (719) 486-2176
Tee Times: (719) 486-2176

Tee Time Info: (resident): 6 day advance
(non-resident): 6 day advance

Green Fees: (resident): $11.00

(non-resident): $11.00

Credit Cards: Master Card, Visa, Discover
Discounts: no

Number of Holes: 9
Number of Courses on Site: 1

	Championship Tees	Men's Tees	Ladies' Tees
Par:	36	36	36
Length:	6350	6050	4950
Course Rating:	68.6	67.7	71.6
Slope:	120	117	120

Year Opened: 1972

Golf Carts Available: yes   **Cart Fee:** $10.00
Driving Range: yes
On Site Lodging: no

Tournaments: yes

Annual Number of Golf Days: 175
Total Rounds Played Annually: 15,000

General Manager: Craig Stuller
Head Pro: Geoff Wauga
Superintendent: Craig Stuller

Designer/Architect: Aldoph Stuller
Average Play Time: 3:50
Special Features: pro shop, restaurant

Patty Jewett Golf Course - 18

Address: 900 East Española
Colorado Springs,CO 80907

Phone #: (719) 578-6826
Tee Times: (719) 578-6827

Tee Time Info: (resident): 7 day advance
(non-resident): 7 day advance

Green Fees: (resident): $13.00

(non-resident): $13.00

Credit Cards: no
Discounts: no

Number of Holes: 18
Number of Courses on Site: 2

	Championship Tees	Men's Tees	Ladies' Tees
Par:	72	72	75
Length:	6811	6463	5998
Course Rating:	71.5	69.9	73.0
Slope:	124	120	124

Year Opened: 1898

Golf Carts Available: yes   **Cart Fee:** $16.00
Driving Range: no
On Site Lodging: no

Tournaments: yes

Annual Number of Golf Days: 315
Total Rounds Played Annually: 180,000

General Manager: Scott Simpson
Head Pro: Paul Ramson
Superintendent: Pat Gintilly

Designer/Architect: Willie Campbell
Average Play Time: 3:55
Special Features: restaurant, oldest course west of the Mississippi

Patty Jewett Golf Course - 9

Address: 900 East Española
Colorado Springs, CO 80907

Phone #: (719) 578-6826
Tee Times: (719) 578-6827

Tee Time Info: (resident): 7 day advance
(non-resident): 7 day advance

Green Fees: (resident): $13.00

(non-resident): $13.00

Credit Cards: no
Discounts: no

Number of Holes: 9
Number of Courses on Site: 2

	Championship Tees	Men's Tees	Ladies' Tees
Par:	68	68	74
Length:	6320	6012	5748
Course Rating:	67.5	Not Available At Time Of Press	Not Available At Time Of Press
Slope:	Not Available At Time Of Press	Not Available At Time Of Press	110

Year Opened: 1898

Golf Carts Available: yes   **Cart Fee:** $8.00
Driving Range: no
On Site Lodging: no

Tournaments: yes

Annual Number of Golf Days: 315
Total Rounds Played Annually: 180,000

General Manager: Scott Simpson
Head Pro: Paul Ramson
Superintendent: Pat Gintilly

Designer/Architect: Willie Campbell
Average Play Time: 3:47 (18 holes)
Special Features: restaurant, oldest course west of the Mississippi

Pine Creek Golf Club

Address: 9850 Divot Trail
Colorado Springs, CO 80920

Phone #: (719) 594-9999
Tee Times: (719) 594-9999

Tee Time Info: (resident): 7 day advance
(non-resident): 3 day advance

Green Fees: **(resident):** $21.00 weekday
$25.00 weekend
(non-resident): $21.00 weekday
$25.00 weekend
Credit Cards: Master Card, Visa
Discounts: no

Number of Holes: 18
Number of Courses on Site: 1

	Championship Tees	Men's Tees	Ladies' Tees
Par:	72	72	72
Length:	6579	6040	5314
Course Rating:	70.4	68.0	69.0
Slope:	132	123	113

Year Opened: 1988

Golf Carts Available: yes   **Cart Fee:** $20.00
Driving Range: yes
On Site Lodging: no

Tournaments: yes

Annual Number of Golf Days: 300
Total Rounds Played Annually: 53,000

General Manager: Mike Brennan
Head Pro: Larry Mullis III
Superintendent: Eric Hothen

Designer/Architect: Dick Phelps
Average Play Time: 4:05
Special Features: 73 bunkers, 4 lakes, 4 dry creek beds

Salida Golf Club

Address: Crestone Avenue & Grant Street
Salida, CO 81201-1586

Phone #:   (970) 539-1060
Tee Times: (970) 539-1060

Tee Time Info: **(resident):**   2 day advance
                (non-resident): 2 day advance

Green Fees: **(resident):** $18.00

                (non-resident): $18.00

Credit Cards: Master Card, Visa
Discounts: yes

Number of Holes: 9
Number of Courses on Site: 1

	Championship Tees	Men's Tees	Ladies' Tees
Par:	no	70	70
Length:	no	6360	5718
Course Rating:	no	68.8	71.0
Slope:	no	118	118

Year Opened: 1927

Golf Carts Available: yes   **Cart Fee:** $18.00
Driving Range: yes
On Site Lodging: no

Tournaments: yes

Annual Number of Golf Days: 250
Total Rounds Played Annually: 22,000

General Manager: no
Head Pro: Lori Mitchell
Superintendent: Jim Luchetta

Designer/Architect:
Average Play Time: 3:34
Special Features: clubhouse, pro shop, restaurant

St. Andrews at Westcliffe

Address: 800 Copper Gulch Road
P.O. Box 807
Westcliffe, CO 81252
Phone #: (719) 783-9410, (800) 258-9410
Tee Times: (719) 783-9410, (800) 258-9410

Tee Time Info: (resident): advance recommended for weekends
(non-resident): advance recommended for weekends

Green Fees: (resident): $15.00

(non-resident): $15.00

Credit Cards: Master Card, Visa, Discover
Discounts: low season, early bird

Number of Holes: 9
Number of Courses on Site: 1

	Championship Tees	Men's Tees	Ladies' Tees
Par:	70	70	70
Length:	6088	5488	4828
Course Rating:	64.9	64.6	Not Available At Time Of Press
Slope:	114	110	Not Available At Time Of Press

Year Opened: 1989

Golf Carts Available: yes   **Cart Fee:** $16.50
Driving Range: yes
On Site Lodging: no

Tournaments: yes

Annual Number of Golf Days: 254
Total Rounds Played Annually: 5,000

General Manager: Dave Peters, Darlene Peters
Head Pro: Ken McGruther
Superintendent: Pamela Zika

Designer/Architect: John Manson
Average Play Time: 3:36
Special Features: rental clubs, clubhouse, snack bar

Shadow Hills Golf Club

Address: 1232 County Road 143
P.O. Box 931
Cañon City, CO 81215
Phone #:   (719) 275-0603
Tee Times: (719) 275-0603

Tee Time Info: (resident):   1 day advance (weekdays), Fri. (weekends)
(non-resident):   1 day advance (weekdays), Fr. (weekends)

Green Fees: **(resident):**   memberships

(non-resident): $20.00

Credit Cards: no
Discounts: no

Number of Holes: 9
Number of Courses on Site: 1

	Championship Tees	Men's Tees	Ladies' Tees
Par:	yes	72	72
Length:	yes	6160	5326
Course Rating:	yes	68.7	67.8
Slope:	yes	109	109

Year Opened: 1959

Golf Carts Available: yes   **Cart Fee:** $15.00
Driving Range: yes
On Site Lodging: no

Tournaments: yes

Annual Number of Golf Days: 300
Total Rounds Played Annually: 23,300

General Manager: Don Mosgrove
Head Pro: Greg Dillon
Superintendent: Mike Pratz

Designer/Architect: Keith Foster
Average Play Time: 3:42
Special Features: pro shop, restaurant

Valley Hi Golf Course

Address: 610 South Chelton
Colorado Springs, CO 80910

Phone #: (719) 578-6926
Tee Times: (719) 578-6351

Tee Time Info: (resident): 7 day advance
(non-resident): 7 day advance

Green Fees: (resident): $13.00

(non-resident): $13.00

Credit Cards: Master Card, Visa
Discounts: seniors, juniors

Number of Holes: 18
Number of Courses on Site: 1

	Championship Tees	Men's Tees	Ladies' Tees
Par:	71	71	73
Length:	6806	6392	5404
Course Rating:	71.1	69.3	68.7
Slope:	116	112	109

Year Opened: 1964

Golf Carts Available: yes   **Cart Fee:** $16.00
Driving Range: yes
On Site Lodging: no

Tournaments: yes

Annual Number of Golf Days: 320
Total Rounds Played Annually: 85,000

General Manager: no
Head Pro: Mike Northern
Superintendent: Mike Cooper

Designer/Architect:
Average Play Time: 3:58
Special Features: pro shop, restaurant

Woodland Park Fujiki Golf & C.C.

Address: 100 Lucky Lady Drive
Woodland Park, CO 80863

Phone #: (719) 687-7587
Tee Times: (719) 687-7587

Tee Time Info: (resident): 3 day advance
(non-resident): 3 day advance

Green Fees: (resident): $45.00 weekday
$55.00 weekend
(non-resident): $45.00 weekday
$55.00 weekend
Credit Cards: Master Card, Visa, American Express, Discover
Discounts: packages

Number of Holes: 18
Number of Courses on Site: 1

	Championship Tees	Men's Tees	Ladies' Tees
Par:	Not Available At Press	Not Available At Press	Not Available At Press
Length:	6707	6445	6089
Course Rating:	71.5	70.3	68.8
Slope:	129	125	119

Year Opened: 1995

Golf Carts Available: yes　　　　　**Cart Fee:** $20.00
Driving Range: proposed for June or July, 1995
On Site Lodging: no

Tournaments: yes

Annual Number of Golf Days: opened 1995
Total Rounds Played Annually: opened 1995

Head Pro: Ray Blew
Superintendent: Grant Yaklich

Designer/Architect: John Harbottle
Average Play Time: 4:15 (estimate)
Special Features: clubhouse, pro shop, practice chipping area

SOUTH WEST REGION

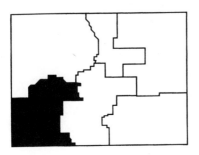

Conquistador Golf Club

Address: 2018 North Dolores Road
Cortez, CO 81321

Phone #: (970) 565-9208
Tee Times: (970) 565-9208

Tee Time Info: (resident): 2 day advance
(non-resident): 2 day advance

Green Fees: (resident): $14.00

(non-resident): $14.00

Credit Cards: no
Discounts: no

Number of Holes: 18
Number of Courses on Site: 1

	Championship Tees	Men's Tees	Ladies' Tees
Par:	72	72	72
Length:	6832	6347	5563
Course Rating:	70.4	68.3	69.5
Slope:	113	109	110

Year Opened: 1955

Golf Carts Available: yes   **Cart Fee:** $18.00
Driving Range: yes
On Site Lodging: no

Tournaments: yes

Annual Number of Golf Days: 258
Total Rounds Played Annually: 19,592

General Manager: Roland Rudosky
Head Pro: Roland Rudosky
Superintendent: Ed Hellam

Designer/Architect: Press Maxwell
Average Play Time: 3:49
Special Features: pro shop, restaurant

Cottonwood Golf Course

Address: 1679 Highway 75 Road
               Delta, CO 81416

Phone #:   (970) 874-7263
Tee Times: (970) 874-7263

Tee Time Info: **(resident):**   2 day advance
                (non-resident): 2 day advance

Green Fees: **(resident):** $10.00 weekday
                              $11.00 weekend
                (non-resident): $10.00 weekday
                              $11.00 weekend
Credit Cards: Master Card, Visa
Discounts: seniors

Number of Holes: 9
Number of Courses on Site: 1

	Championship Tees	Men's Tees	Ladies' Tees
Par:	72	72	72
Length:	6324	6324	5402
Course Rating:	73.2	66.9	69.0
Slope:	115	112	107

Year Opened: 1926

Golf Carts Available: yes   **Cart Fee:** $14.00
Driving Range: yes
On Site Lodging: no

Tournaments: yes

Annual Number of Golf Days: 220
Total Rounds Played Annually: 25,000

General Manager: Randy Burross
Head Pro: Randy Burross
Superintendent: Rod Meyers

Designer/Architect: H. Showalter
Average Play Time: 3:51
Special Features: pro shop, restaurant

Dalton Ranch and Golf Club

Address: 589 County Road 252
P.O. Box 2705
Durango, CO 81302
Phone #:   (970) 247-8774
Tee Times: (970) 247-8774

Tee Time Info: **(resident):**   first priority (members)
              (non-resident): 7 day advance

Green Fees: **(resident):**   (no fee for members)
                             $20.00 (guests)
          (non-resident): $38.00

Credit Cards: Master Card, Visa
Discounts: low season

Number of Holes: 18
Number of Courses on Site: 1

	Championship Tees	Men's Tees	Ladies' Tees
Par:	72	72	72
Length:	6934	6394	5539
Course Rating:	72.4	70.1	71.7
Slope:	135	125	125

Year Opened: 1993

Golf Carts Available: yes   **Cart Fee:** $9.00
Driving Range: yes
On Site Lodging: no

Tournaments: yes

Annual Number of Golf Days: 210
Total Rounds Played Annually: 14,000

General Manager: Frank Sinton
Head Pro: Fal Wood
Superintendent: John Finsterwald

Designer/Architect: Ken Dye
Average Play Time: 4:09
Special Features: locker rooms, tennis courts, swimming pool

Deercreek Village Golf Club

Address: 500 Southeast Jay Avenue
P.O. Box 398
Cedaredge, CO 81413
Phone #: (970) 856-7781
Tee Times: (970) 856-7781

Tee Time Info: (resident): 7 day advance
(non-resident): 7 day advance

Green Fees: (resident): $17.00

(non-resident): $17.00

Credit Cards: Master Card, Visa, Discover
Discounts: no

Number of Holes: 9
Number of Courses on Site: 1

	Championship Tees	Men's Tees	Ladies' Tees
Par:	72	72	72
Length:	6436	5920	4926
Course Rating:	68.6	68.6	66.2
Slope:	120	120	115

Year Opened: 1992

Golf Carts Available: yes **Cart Fee:** $18.00
Driving Range: yes
On Site Lodging: no

Tournaments: yes

Annual Number of Golf Days: 275
Total Rounds Played Annually: 30,000

General Manager: Bob Marah
Head Pro: Eric Feely
Superintendent: Mark Bogart

Designer/Architect: Byron Coker
Average Play Time: 3:40
Special Features: pro shop, snack bar, view, restaurant

Dos Rios Country Club

Address: 501 Camino Del Rio Drive
Gunnison, CO 81230

Phone #:   (970) 641-1482
Tee Times: (970) 641-1482

Tee Time Info: (resident):   2 day advance
                     (non-resident): 2 day advance

Green Fees: **(resident):** $10.00

              (non-resident): $10.00

Credit Cards: Master Card, Visa
Discounts: yes

Number of Holes: 18
Number of Courses on Site: 1

	Championship Tees	Men's Tees	Ladies' Tees
Par:	71	71	71
Length:	6575	6070	5505
Course Rating:	68.9	66.6	70.0
Slope:	126	118	118

Year Opened: 1962, 1981

Golf Carts Available: yes   **Cart Fee:** $14.00
Driving Range: yes
On Site Lodging: no

Tournaments: yes

Annual Number of Golf Days: 220
Total Rounds Played Annually: 25,000

General Manager: Brian Erickson
Head Pro: Brian Erickson
Superintendent: George Stowell

Designer/Architect: Press Maxwell, Dick Phelps
Average Play Time: 3:56
Special Features: Pro shop, restaurant

Fairfield Pagosa - Pinon Meadows

Address: P.O. Box 4040
Pagosa Springs, CO 81157

Phone #:   (970) 731-4123, (970) 731-4755
Tee Times: (970) 731-4123, (970) 731-4755

Tee Time Info: (resident):   Information not available at time of press
           (non-resident): Information not availalbe at time of press

Green Fees: **(resident):** $24.00 (resort guests)

                (non-resident): $30.00

Credit Cards: Master Card, Visa, American Express
Discounts: no

Number of Holes: 18
Number of Courses on Site: 3

	Championship Tees	Men's Tees	Ladies' Tees
Par:	72	72	72
Length:	7241	6466	5380
Course Rating:	72.9	69.4	69.1
Slope:	125	118	112

Year Opened: 1988 (Meadows)

Golf Carts Available: yes   **Cart Fee:** included
Driving Range: yes
On Site Lodging: yes

Tournaments: yes

Annual Number of Golf Days: 237
Total Rounds Played Annually: 22,830

General Manager: Arne Fremstad
Head Pro: Arne Fremstad
Superintendent: Terry Carter

Designer/Architect: Rees Jones (Meadows), Johnny Bulla (Pinon)
Average Play Time: 3:58
Special Features: pro shop, Great Divide Restaurant, tennis

Fairfield Pagosa - Pinon Ponderosa

Address: P.O. Box 4040
Pagosa Springs, CO 81157

Phone #: (970) 731-4123, (970) 731-4755
Tee Times: (970) 731-4123, (970) 731-4755

Tee Time Info: (resident): Information not available at time of press
(non-resident): Information not available at time of press

Green Fees: **(resident):** $24.00 (resort guests)

(non-resident): $30.00

Credit Cards: Master Card, Visa, American Express
Discounts: no

Number of Holes: 18
Number of Courses on Site: 3

	Championship Tees	Men's Tees	Ladies' Tees
Par:	71	71	71
Length:	6690	6236	5378
Course Rating:	69.4	67.9	69.0
Slope:	119	115	112

Golf Carts Available: yes   **Cart Fee:** included
Driving Range: yes
On Site Lodging: yes

Tournaments: yes

Annual Number of Golf Days: 237
Total Rounds Played Annually: 22,830

General Manager: Arne Fremstad
Head Pro: Arne Fremstad
Superintendent: Terry Carter

Designer/Architect: Johnny Bulla
Average Play Time: 3:45
Special Features: pro shop, Great Divide Restaurant, tennis

Fairfield Pagosa-Ponderosa Meadows

Address: P.O. Box 4040
Pagosa Springs, CO 81157

Phone #:   (970) 731-4123, (970) 731-4755
Tee Times: (970) 731-4123, (970) 731-4755

Tee Time Info: (resident):   Information not available at time of press
             (non-resident): Information not available at time of press

Green Fees: **(resident):** $24.00 (resort guests)

               (non-resident): $30.00

Credit Cards: Master Card, Visa, American Express
Discounts: no

Number of Holes: 18
Number of Courses on Site: 3

	Championship Tees	Men's Tees	Ladies' Tees
Par:	71	71	71
Length:	6913	6074	5112
Course Rating:	70.9	67.9	67.3
Slope:	123	116	110

Year Opened: 1988 (Meadows)

Golf Carts Available: yes   **Cart Fee:** included
Driving Range: yes
On Site Lodging: yes

Tournaments: yes

Annual Number of Golf Days: 237
Total Rounds Played Annually: 22,830

General Manager: Arne Fremstad
Head Pro: Arne Fremstad
Superintendent: Terry Carter

Designer/Architect: Rees Jones-Meadows, Johnny Bulla-Ponderosa
Average Play Time: 3:50
Special Features: pro shop, Great Divide Restaurant, tennis
swimming pool

Hillcrest Golf Course

Address: 2300 Rim Drive
Durango, CO 81301

Phone #:   (970) 247-1499
Tee Times: (970) 247-1499

Tee Time Info: (resident):   7 day advance
(non-resident): 7 day advance

Green Fees: (resident): $15.00

(non-resident): $15.00

Credit Cards: Master Card, Visa
Discounts: no

Number of Holes: 18
Number of Courses on Site: 1

	Championship Tees	Men's Tees	Ladies' Tees
Par:	71	71	71
Length:	6838	6399	5252
Course Rating:	71.3	69.3	68.1
Slope:	127	120	111

Year Opened: 1969

Golf Carts Available: yes   **Cart Fee:** $15.00
Driving Range: yes
On Site Lodging: no

Tournaments: yes

Annual Number of Golf Days: 240
Total Rounds Played Annually: 45,000

General Manager: no
Head Pro: Jim Fiala
Superintendent: Rick Kern

Designer/Architect: Frank Hummel
Average Play Time: 3:51
Special Features: snack bar, pro shop, putting green, fast greens

Montrose Golf Course

Address: 1350 Birch Street
Montrose, CO 81401

Phone #: (970) 249-8551
Tee Times: (970) 249-8551

Tee Time Info: (resident): 3 day advance
(non-resident): 3 day advance

Green Fees: **(resident):** $20.00

(non-resident): $20.00

Credit Cards: Master Card, Visa
Discounts: twilight

Number of Holes: 18
Number of Courses on Site: 1

	Championship Tees	Men's Tees	Ladies' Tees
Par:	72	72	72
Length:	6446	6258	5676
Course Rating:	69.2	68.4	70.7
Slope:	129	127	114

Year Opened: 1960

Golf Carts Available: yes   **Cart Fee:** $10 per player
Driving Range: no
On Site Lodging: no

Tournaments: yes

Annual Number of Golf Days: 237
Total Rounds Played Annually: 35,000

General Manager: Brian Ryall
Head Pro: Brian Ryall
Superintendent: Doug deVries

Designer/Architect: Joe Francese
Average Play Time: 3:48
Special Features: pro shop

Skyland Mountain Golf Resort

Address: 385 Country Club Drive
P.O. Box 879
Crested Butte, CO 81224
Phone #: (970) 349-6129, (800) 628-5496
Tee Times: (970) 349-6129, (800) 628-5496

Tee Time Info: (resident): several day / week advance
(non-resident): several day / week advance

Green Fees: **(resident):** $70.00

(non-resident): $70.00

Credit Cards: Master Card, Visa, American Express
Discounts: low season, twilight

Number of Holes: 18
Number of Courses on Site: 1

	Championship Tees	Men's Tees	Ladies' Tees
Par:	72	72	72
Length:	6635	6368	5702
Course Rating:	69.8	68.4	72.4
Slope:	121	117	123

Year Opened: 1983

Golf Carts Available: yes (mandatory)   **Cart Fee:** $15.00
Driving Range: yes
On Site Lodging: yes

Tournaments: yes

Annual Number of Golf Days: 160
Total Rounds Played Annually: 18,500

General Manager: Tina Wilkerson, CPA (Controller)
Head Pro: Kirk Cavarra
Superintendent: Stephen Rau

Designer/Architect: Robert Trent Jones Jr.
Average Play Time: 4:14
Special Features: 30,000 square foot clubhouse, pro shop, restaurant

Tamarron Golf Course

Address: 40292 US Highway 550 North
P.O. Box 3131
Durango, CO 81302
Phone #:   (970) 259-2000, (800) 678-1000
Tee Times: (970) 259-2000, (800) 678-1000

Tee Time Info: (resident):   2 day advance (resort guests)
    (non-resident): phone day of play

Green Fees: **(resident):** $95.00 (resort guests)

    (non-resident): $115.00

Credit Cards: all major
Discounts: low season, resort guests

Number of Holes: 18
Number of Courses on Site: 1

	Championship Tees	Men's Tees	Ladies' Tees
Par:	72	72	72
Length:	6885	6340	5330
Course Rating:	73.0	70.6	71.9
Slope:	144	139	127

Year Opened: 1975

Golf Carts Available: yes   **Cart Fee:** included
Driving Range: yes
On Site Lodging: yes

Tournaments: yes

Annual Number of Golf Days: 225
Total Rounds Played Annually: 18,300

General Manager: Bob Nelson
Head Pro: Steve Nichols
Superintendent: Steve Nichols

Designer/Architect: Arthur Hills
Average Play Time: 4:30
Special Features: 750 acres surrounded by San Juan National Forest

Telluride Golf Club

Address: 562 Mountain Village Boulevard
P.O. Box 11155
Telluride, CO 81435
Phone #: (970) 728-6366
Tee Times: (970) 728-6366

Tee Time Info: (resident): 30 day advance (resort guests)
(non-resident): 1 day advance

Green Fees: (resident): $83.00 (resort guests)

(non-resident): $95.00

Credit Cards: Master Card, Visa
Discounts: twilight, low season

Number of Holes: 18
Number of Courses on Site: 1

	Championship Tees	Men's Tees	Ladies' Tees
Par:	71	71	71
Length:	6739	6277	5181
Course Rating:	71.0	68.9	66.3
Slope:	130	125	120

Year Opened: 1992

Golf Carts Available: mandatory   **Cart Fee:** included
Driving Range: yes
On Site Lodging: yes

Tournaments: yes

Annual Number of Golf Days: 130
Total Rounds Played Annually: 8,000 - 10,000

General Manager: no
Head Pro: Murray Odegaard
Superintendent: Kevin Cahalane

Designer/Architect: Telluride Ski and Golf Co.
Average Play Time: 4:06
Special Features: pro shop, restaurant, 14,000' mountain peaks

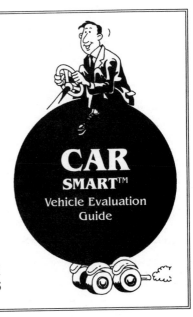

NORTH WEST REGION

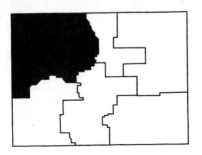

Northwest Region

Adobe Creek National Golf Course

Address: 876 18 1/2 Road
Fruita, CO 81521

Phone #:   (970) 858-0521
Tee Times: (970) 858-0521

Tee Time Info: (resident):   2 day advance
(non-resident):   2 day advance

Green Fees: (resident): $16.00 weekday
$22.00 weekend
(non-resident): $16.00 weekday
$22.00 weekend
Credit Cards: Mater Card, Visa
Discounts: no

Number of Holes: 18
Number of Courses on Site: 1

	Championship Tees	Men's Tees	Ladies' Tees
Par:	72	72	72
Length:	6997	6447	4980
Course Rating:	71.2	67.6	no rating
Slope:	118	108	no record

Year Opened: 1992

Golf Carts Available: yes   **Cart Fee:** $16.00
Driving Range: yes
On Site Lodging: no

Tournaments: yes

Annual Number of Golf Days: 295
Total Rounds Played Annually: 12,000

General Manager: Tim Doherty
Head Pro: Steve Pettit
Superintendent: Ned Wilson

Designer/Architect: Ned Wilson
Average Play Time: 3:51
Special Features: clubhouse, open layout, Scottish Links style

Aspen Golf Course

Address: 408 East Cooper
Aspen, CO 81611

Phone #:   (970) 925-2145
Tee Times: (970) 925-2145

Tee Time Info: (resident):   3 day advance
(non-resident): 3 day advance

Green Fees: (resident): $60.00

(non-resident): $60.00

Credit Cards: Master Card, Visa, Discover
Discounts: low season

Number of Holes: 18
Number of Courses on Site: 1

	Championship Tees	Men's Tees	Ladies' Tees
Par:	71	71	72
Length:	7165	6469	5591
Course Rating:	72.2	69.0	69.0
Slope:	125	118	116

Year Opened: 1979

Golf Carts Available: yes   **Cart Fee:** $25.00
Driving Range: yes
On Site Lodging: no

Tournaments: yes

Annual Number of Golf Days: 180
Total Rounds Played Annually: 35,000

General Manager: Ernie Fyrwald
Head Pro: Alden Richards, Jr.
Superintendent: Steve Atkin

Designer/Architect: Frank Hummel
Average Play Time: 4:00
Special Features: Links style

Battlement Mesa Golf Club

Address: 3930 North Battlement Parkway
P.O. Box 6000
Battlement Mesa, CO 81636
Phone #: (970) 285-7274
Tee Times: (970) 285-7274

Tee Time Info: (resident): first priority
(non-resident): 3 day advance

Green Fees: **(resident):** $24.00

(non-resident): $24.00

Credit Cards: Master Card, Visa, American Express, Discover
Discounts: low season, seniors, resort guests, residents

Number of Holes: 18
Number of Courses on Site: 1

	Championship Tees	Men's Tees	Ladies' Tees
Par:	72	72	72
Length:	7309	6037	5386
Course Rating:	73.9	69.6	69.9
Slope:	132	120	112

Year Opened: 1987

Golf Carts Available: yes   **Cart Fee:** $12 per player
Driving Range: yes
On Site Lodging: yes

Tournaments: yes

Annual Number of Golf Days: 236
Total Rounds Played Annually: 27,300

General Manager: Johnny Goodman
Head Pro: Johnny Goodman
Superintendent: Ken Seidel

Designer/Architect: Joe Finger, Ken Dye
Average Play Time: 4:04
Special Features: clubhouse, pro shop, snack bar, full service bar

Beaver Creek Golf Club

Address: 103 Offerson Road
              P.O. Box 7
              Avon, CO 81658
Phone #:   (970) 949-7123
Tee Times: (970) 949-7123

Tee Time Info: (resident):   with accommodation reservation
                  (non-resident):   not available during peak season

Green Fees: **(resident):** $100.00

               (non-resident):   not available during peak season

Credit Cards: all major
Discounts: low season

Number of Holes: 18
Number of Courses on Site: 1

	Championship Tees	Men's Tees	Ladies' Tees
Par:	70	70	70
Length:	6464	6026	5268
Course Rating:	69.2	67.0	69.4
Slope:	133	128	127

Year Opened: 1982

Golf Carts Available: yes (mandatory)   **Cart Fee:** included
Driving Range: yes
On Site Lodging: yes

Tournaments: yes

Annual Number of Golf Days: 173
Total Rounds Played Annually: 20,000

Head Pro: Tom Clary

Designer/Architect: Robert Trent Jones, Jr.
Average Play Time: 3:51
Special Features: pro shop, restaurant

Breckenridge Golf Club

Address: 200 Clubhouse Drive
P.O. Box 7965
Breckenridge, CO 80424
Phone #: (970) 453-9104
Tee Times: (970) 453-9104

Tee Time Info: (resident): 2 day advance
(non-resident): 2 day advance

Green Fees: **(resident):** $75.00

(non-resident): $75.00

Credit Cards: Master Card, Visa, American Express
Discounts: twilight, low season

Number of Holes: 18
Number of Courses on Site: 1

	Championship Tees	Men's Tees	Ladies' Tees
Par:	72	72	72
Length:	7279	5980	5066
Course Rating:	73.1	66.9	67.7
Slope:	146	128	118

Year Opened: 1985

Golf Carts Available: yes   **Cart Fee:** included
Driving Range: yes
On Site Lodging: no

Tournaments: yes

Annual Number of Golf Days: 180
Total Rounds Played Annually: 23,300

Head Pro: Erroll Miller
Superintendent: Jack Pendleton

Designer/Architect: Jack Nicklaus
Average Play Time: 4:36
Special Features: Colorado's Best Public course, Golf Digest Oct. '91

Cedar Ridges Golf Course

Address: 502 County Road #108
P.O. Box 370
Rangley, CO 81648
Phone #:   (970) 675-8403
Tee Times: (970) 675-8403

Tee Time Info: (resident):   advanced tee times not available
           (non-resident): advanced tee times not available

Green Fees: **(resident):** $6.00 weekday
                           $8.00 weekend
              (non-resident): $6.00 weekday
                           $8.00 weekend
Credit Cards: Master Card, Visa
Discounts: juniors

Number of Holes: 9
Number of Courses on Site: 1

	Championship Tees	Men's Tees	Ladies' Tees
Par:	72	72	72
Length:	6866	6281	5878
Course Rating:	71.4	68.5	71.6
Slope:	123	117	113

Year Opened: 1985

Golf Carts Available: yes   **Cart Fee:** $8.00
Driving Range: yes
On Site Lodging: no

Tournaments: yes

Annual Number of Golf Days: 199
Total Rounds Played Annually: 24,500

General Manager: Hans G. Parkinson
Head Pro: Hans G. Parkinson
Superintendent: Bernie Schafer

Designer/Architect: Frank Hummel
Average Play Time: 3:51
Special Features: pro shop, restaurant

Copper Creek Golf Club

Address: 104 Wheeler Place
              P.O. Box 3415
              Copper Mountain, CO 80443
Phone #: (970) 968-2882
Tee Times: (970) 968-2882

Tee Time Info: (resident): 60 day advance (resort guests)
                   (non-resident): 4 day advance

Green Fees: **(resident):** $52.00 (resort guests)

              (non-resident): $65.00

Credit Cards: all major
Discounts: twilight

Number of Holes: 18
Number of Courses on Site: 1

	Championship Tees	Men's Tees	Ladies' Tees
Par:	70	70	70
Length:	6094	5742	5159
Course Rating:	67.6	65.9	63.0
Slope:	124	117	110

Golf Carts Available: yes   **Cart Fee:** included
Driving Range: yes
On Site Lodging: yes

Tournaments: yes

Annual Number of Golf Days: 185
Total Rounds Played Annually: 15,260

General Manager: Rick Fretland
Head Pro: Rick Fretland
Superintendent: Dave Balerud

Designer/Architect: Pete Dye, Perry Dye
Average Play Time: 4:08
Special Features: North America's highest elevation 18-hole
                     championship golf course at 9,700'

Eagles Nest Golf Club

Address: 305 Golden Eagle Road
P.O. Box 617
Silverthorne, CO 80498
Phone #:   (970) 468-0681
Tee Times: (970) 468-0681

Tee Time Info: (resident):   7 day advance
                (non-resident): 7 day advance

Green Fees: **(resident):** $55.00 weekday
                                $70.00 weekend
             (non-resident): $55.00 weekday
                                $70.00 weekend
Credit Cards: Master Card, Visa
Discounts: low season, twilight, resort guest

Number of Holes: 18
Number of Courses on Site: 1

	Championship Tees	Men's Tees	Ladies' Tees
Par:	72	72	72
Length:	7024	6658	5556
Course Rating:	72.6	71.5	71.9
Slope:	141	139	126

Year Opened: 1985

Golf Carts Available: yes   **Cart Fee:** included
Driving Range: yes
On Site Lodging: no

Tournaments: yes

Annual Number of Golf Days: 180
Total Rounds Played Annually: 21,000

General Manager: Winston Howe III
Head Pro: Winston Howe III
Superintendent: Jessie Hernandez, Jr.

Designer/Architect: Dick Phelps
Average Play Time: 4:11
Special Features: pro shop

Eagle Vail Golf Club

Address: 431 Eagle Drive
P.O. Box 5660
Avon, CO 81620
Phone #:   (970) 949-5267
Tee Times: (970) 949-5267

Tee Time Info: (resident): 2 day advance
(non-resident): 2 day advance

Green Fees: **(resident):** $60.00

   (non-resident): $60.00

Credit Cards: Master Card, Visa, American Express
Discounts: low season, twilight

Number of Holes: 18
Number of Courses on Site: 1

	Championship Tees	Men's Tees	Ladies' Tees
Par:	72	72	72
Length:	6819	6168	4856
Course Rating:	70.9	68.7	67.3
Slope:	131	123	114

Year Opened: 1975

Golf Carts Available: yes   **Cart Fee:** $15.00
Driving Range: yes
On Site Lodging: no

Tournaments: yes

Annual Number of Golf Days: 180
Total Rounds Played Annually: 25,000

General Manager: no
Head Pro: Mike Fox
Superintendent: Jan Niedziela

Designer/Architect: Bruce Devlin, Bob Von Hagge
Average Play Time: 3:50
Special Features: clubhouse, restaurant, swimming pool

Glenwood Springs Golf Course

Address: 193 Sunny Acres Road
P.O. Box 2298
Glenwood Springs, CO 81602
Phone #:   (970) 945-7086
Tee Times: (970) 945-7086

Tee Time Info: (resident):   7 day advance
                 (non-resident): 7 day advance

Green Fees: **(resident):** $17.00

               (non-resident): $23.00

Credit Cards: Master Card, Visa
Discounts: juniors

Number of Holes: 9
Number of Courses on Site: 1

	Championship Tees	Men's Tees	Ladies' Tees
Par:	70	70	70
Length:	5812	5517	5260
Course Rating:	66.1	65.9	67.9
Slope:	106	106	108

Year Opened: 1946

Golf Carts Available: yes   **Cart Fee:** $18.00
Driving Range: no
On Site Lodging: no

Tournaments: no

Annual Number of Golf Days: 190
Total Rounds Played Annually: 23,333

General Manager: Greg Gortsema
Head Pro: Greg Gortsema
Superintendent: Jim Richmond

Average Play Time: 3:47
Special Features: pro shop, restaurant

Grand Lake Golf Course

Address: 1415 County Road 48
P.O. Box 590
Grand Lake, CO 80447
Phone #: (970) 627-8008
Tee Times: (970) 627-8008

Tee Time Info: (resident): Phone Thursday for weekend
(non-resident): Phone Thursday for weekend

Green Fees: **(resident):** $40.00

(non-resident): $40.00

Credit Cards: Master Card, Visa
Discounts: no

Number of Holes: 18
Number of Courses on Site: 1

	Championship Tees	Men's Tees	Ladies' Tees
Par:	72	72	74
Length:	6542	6324	5685
Course Rating:	70.5	69.4	70.9
Slope:	131	128	123

Year Opened: 1964

Golf Carts Available: yes   **Cart Fee:** $23.00
Driving Range: yes
On Site Lodging: no

Tournaments: yes

Annual Number of Golf Days: 135
Total Rounds Played Annually: 20,040

General Manager: John Dill
Head Pro: John Dill

Designer/Architect: Dick Phelps
Average Play Time: 3:52
Special Features: clubhouse, tennis courts, pro shop, restaurant

Keystone Ranch Golf Course

Address: Highway 6
Keystone, CO 80435

Phone #:   (970) 468-4250, (800) 451-5930
Tee Times: (970) 468-4FUN, (800) 354-4FUN

Tee Time Info: (resident):   7 day advance (resort guests)
(non-resident): 4 day advance

Green Fees: **(resident):** $82.00 (resort guests)

(non-resident): $92.00

Credit Cards: all major
Discounts: low season, twilight, memberships

Number of Holes: 18
Number of Courses on Site: 1

	Championship Tees	Men's Tees	Ladies' Tees
Par:	72	72	72
Length:	7090	6521	5596
Course Rating:	72.3	69.9	70.7
Slope:	136	130	129

Year Opened: 1980

Golf Carts Available: yes   **Cart Fee:** included
Driving Range: yes
On Site Lodging: yes

Tournaments: yes

Annual Number of Golf Days: 140
Total Rounds Played Annually: 17,500

Head Pro: Mike Dahlheim
Superintendent: Steve Corneillier

Designer/Architect: Robert Trent Jones, Jr.
Average Play Time: 4:30
Special Features: One of the top 10 courses in Colorado by Golf Digest

Lincoln Park Golf Course

Address: 8 Mantizo Circle
Grand Junction, CO 81501

Phone #: (970) 242-6394
Tee Times: (970) 242-6394

Tee Time Info: (resident): 2 day advance
(non-resident): 2 day advance

Green Fees: **(resident):** $14.00 weekday
$16.75 weekend
(non-resident): $14.00 weekday
$16.75 weekend
Credit Cards: Master Card, Visa
Discounts: seniors, juniors

Number of Holes: 9
Number of Courses on Site: 1

	Championship Tees	Men's Tees	Ladies' Tees
Par:	no	72	72
Length:	no	6435	6328
Course Rating:	no	68.5	73.9
Slope:	no	114	115

Year Opened: 1929

Golf Carts Available: yes   **Cart Fee:** $16.00
Driving Range: yes
On Site Lodging: no

Tournaments: yes

Annual Number of Golf Days: 270
Total Rounds Played Annually: 46,992

General Manager: Jack Sommers
Head Pro: Dan Adams
Superintendent: Doug Jones

Average Play Time: 3:47
Special Features: pro shop

Meeker Golf Course

Address: 903 County Road 13
P.O. Box 891
Meeker, CO 81641
Phone #: (970) 878-5642
Tee Times: (970) 878-5642

Tee Time Info: (resident): advanced tee times not available
(non-resident): advanced tee times not available

Green Fees: **(resident):** $15.00

(non-resident): $15.00

Credit Cards: no
Discounts: no

Number of Holes: 9
Number of Courses on Site: 1

	Championship Tees	Men's Tees	Ladies' Tees
Par:	68	68	68
Length:	5488	5226	4614
Course Rating:	63.3	Not Available At Press	64.4
Slope:	103	Not Available At Press	100

Golf Carts Available: yes   **Cart Fee:** $15.00
Driving Range: yes
On Site Lodging: no

Tournaments: yes

Annual Number of Golf Days: 250
Total Rounds Played Annually: 13,000

General Manager: Jim Cook
Head Pro: Jim Cook
Superintendent:

Average Play Time: 3:32
Special Features: quiet, not crowded, pro shop

Pole Creek Golf Club

Address: County Road 51
P.O. Box 3348
Winter Park, CO 80482
Phone #: (970) 726-8847
Tee Times: (970) 726-8847

Tee Time Info: **(resident):** 5 day advance
(non-resident): 5 day advance

Green Fees: **(resident):** $55.00 weekday
$60.00 weekend
(non-resident): $55.00 weekday
$60.00 weekend
Credit Cards: Master Card, Visa, Discover
Discounts: low season, twilight, juniors

Number of Holes: 18
Number of Courses on Site: 1

	Championship Tees	Men's Tees	Ladies' Tees
Par:	72	72	72
Length:	7107	6413	5006
Course Rating:	73.1	69.6	69.9
Slope:	135	129	119

Year Opened: 1983

Golf Carts Available: yes   **Cart Fee:** $12.50 per player
Driving Range: yes
On Site Lodging: no

Tournaments: yes

Annual Number of Golf Days: 130
Total Rounds Played Annually: 22,000

General Manager: Conner Shepherd
Head Pro: Kim Anders
Superintendent: Larry Burks

Designer/Architect: Denis Griffiths
Average Play Time: 4:13
Special Features: Best New Public Course of 1985 by <u>Golf Digest</u>

Rifle Creek Golf Course

Address: 3004 State Highway 325
               Rifle, CO 81650

Phone #:   (970) 625-1093
Tee Times: (970) 625-1093

Tee Time Info: (resident):   7 day advance
               (non-resident): 7 day advance

Green Fees: **(resident):** $23.00

               (non-resident): $23.00

Credit Cards: Master Card, Visa
Discounts: low season, twilight

Number of Holes: 18
Number of Courses on Site: 1

	Championship Tees	Men's Tees	Ladies' Tees
Par:	72	72	72
Length:	6241	5751	5131
Course Rating:	69.3	67.0	68.5
Slope:	123	117	109

Year Opened: 1960, 1988

Golf Carts Available: yes   **Cart Fee:** $22.00
Driving Range: yes
On Site Lodging: no

Tournaments: yes

Annual Number of Golf Days: 300
Total Rounds Played Annually: 25,000

General Manager: Steve LeDonne
Head Pro: Steve LeDonne
Superintendent: Dennis Pierce

Designer/Architect: Dick Phelps
Average Play Time: 3:46
Special Features: clubhouse, practice green, pro shop, snack bar

Sheraton Steamboat Resort

Address: 2000 Clubhouse Drive
P.O. Box 774808
Steamboat Springs, CO 80477
Phone #: (970) 879-2220, (800) 848-8877
Tee Times: (970) 879-2220, (970) 879-1391

Tee Time Info: (resident): first priority (resort guests)
(non-resident): 1 day advance

Green Fees: **(resident):** $55.00 (resort guests)

(non-resident): $76.00

Credit Cards: all major
Discounts: low season, twilight

Number of Holes: 18
Number of Courses on Site: 1

	Championship Tees	Men's Tees	Ladies' Tees
Par:	72	72	72
Length:	6906	6276	5647
Course Rating:	71.7	70.0	72.6
Slope:	134	129	127

Year Opened: 1974

Golf Carts Available: yes   **Cart Fee:** $14 per player
Driving Range: yes
On Site Lodging: yes

Tournaments: yes

Annual Number of Golf Days: 150
Total Rounds Played Annually: 16,000

General Manager: Chuck Porter
Head Pro: Hank Franks
Superintendent: Tom Holler

Designer/Architect: Robert Trent Jones, Jr.
Average Play Time: 4:08
Special Features: restaurant, bar, clubhouse, conference center

The Snowmass Club Golf Course

Address: P.O. Box G - 2
Snowmass Village, CO 81615

Phone #: (970) 923-5600, (800) 525-6200
Tee Times: (970) 923-5600

Tee Time Info: (resident): 1 day advance (members)
(non-resident): 1 day advance

Green Fees: (resident): $40.00 (members)

(non-resident): $80.00

Credit Cards: Master Card, Visa, American Express, Discover
Discounts: low season, twilight, resort guests

Number of Holes: 18
Number of Courses on Site: 1

	Championship Tees	Men's Tees	Ladies' Tees
Par:	71	71	71
Length:	6894	6070	5008
Course Rating:	70.5	67.5	67.3
Slope:	134	126	114

Year Opened: 1980

Golf Carts Available: yes   **Cart Fee:** included
Driving Range: yes
On Site Lodging: yes

Tournaments: yes

Annual Number of Golf Days: 175
Total Rounds Played Annually: 25,000

General Manager: Jane Ganoung
Head Pro: Don Buchholz
Superintendent: Al Ogren

Designer/Architect: Arnold Palmer, Ed Seay
Average Play Time: 4:03
Special Features: tennis courts, restaurant, bar, lodge, pro shop, scenic

Sonnenalp Golf Club

Address: 1265 Berry Creek Road
P.O. Box 1080
Edwards, CO 81632
Phone #: (970) 926-3533
Tee Times: (970) 926-3533

Tee Time Info: (resident): 14 day advance (members)
(non-resident): through concierge (hotel guests)

Green Fees: (resident): membership

(non-resident): $110.00

Credit Cards: Master Card, Visa, American Express
Discounts: low season

Number of Holes: 18
Number of Courses on Site: 1

	Championship Tees	Men's Tees	Ladies' Tees
Par:	71	71	71
Length:	7059	6423	5293
Course Rating:	72.3	69.2	70.0
Slope:	138	129	115

Year Opened: 1981

Golf Carts Available: yes (mandatory) **Cart Fee:** $15 per player
Driving Range: yes
On Site Lodging: no

Tournaments: yes

Annual Number of Golf Days: 130
Total Rounds Played Annually: 20,000

General Manager: Martan Abreu
Head Pro: Doug Wall
Superintendent: Michael J. Valiant

Designer/Architect: Robert Cupp, Jay Morrish
Average Play Time: 4:07
Special Features: clubhouse, fast greens, wide landing areas

Tiara Rado Golf Course

Address: 2063 South Broadway
Grand Junction, CO 81503

Phone #: (970) 245-8085
Tee Times: (970) 245-8085

Tee Time Info: (resident): 2 day advance
(non-resident): 2 day advance

Green Fees: (resident): $14.00 weekday
$16.75 weekend
(non-resident): $14.00 weekday
$16.75 weekend
Credit Cards: Master Card, Visa
Discounts: seniors, juniors

Number of Holes: 18
Number of Courses on Site: 1

	Championship Tees	Men's Tees	Ladies' Tees
Par:	71	71	71
Length:	6152	5907	4967
Course Rating:	68.4	67.1	67.0
Slope:	115	112	110

Year Opened: 1971

Golf Carts Available: yes   **Cart Fee:** $17.00
Driving Range: no
On Site Lodging: no

Tournaments: yes

Annual Number of Golf Days: 196
Total Rounds Played Annually: 59,563

General Manager: Jack Sommers
Head Pro: Jack Sommers
Superintendent: Doug Jones

Designer/Architect: Tom Colkolancy
Average Play Time: 3:46
Special Features: clubhouse

Vail Golf Club

Address: 1778 Vail Valley Drive
Vail, CO 81657

Phone #:   (970) 479-2260
Tee Times: (970) 479-2260

Tee Time Info: (resident):   2 day advance
(non-resident): 2 day advance

Green Fees: **(resident):** $45.00

(non-resident): $65.00

Credit Cards: Master Card, Visa
Discounts: no

Number of Holes: 18
Number of Courses on Site: 1

	Championship Tees	Men's Tees	Ladies' Tees
Par:	71	71	72
Length:	7064	6282	5932
Course Rating:	70.8	68.4	72.7
Slope:	121	117	119

Year Opened: 1966

Golf Carts Available: yes   **Cart Fee:** $15 per player
Driving Range: yes
On Site Lodging: no

Tournaments: yes

Annual Number of Golf Days: 200
Total Rounds Played Annually: 32,000

General Manager: Piet Pieters
Head Pro: Steve Satterstrom
Superintendent: Ernie Bender

Designer/Architect: Ben Kreuger
Average Play Time: 4:05
Special Features: pro shop, restaurant, men's and ladies' lockers

Westbank Ranch Golf Course

Address: 1007 Westbank Road
Glenwood Springs, CO 81601

Phone #: (970) 945-7032
Tee Times: (970) 945-7032

Tee Time Info: (resident): 7 day advance
(non-resident): 7 day advance

Green Fees: (resident): $15.00 weekday
$18.00 weekend
(non-resident): $15.00 weekday
$18.00 weekend
Credit Cards: Master Card, Visa
Discounts: seniors, juniors

Number of Holes: 9
Number of Courses on Site: 1

	Championship Tees	Men's Tees	Ladies' Tees
Par:	no	72	72
Length:	no	6345	5866
Course Rating:	no	70.0	71.9
Slope:	no	113	120

Year Opened: 1974

Golf Carts Available: yes   **Cart Fee:** $16.00
Driving Range: yes
On Site Lodging: no

Tournaments: yes

Annual Number of Golf Days: 195
Total Rounds Played Annually: 17,750

General Manager: Bart Victor
Head Pro: Steve Fry
Superintendent: Bart Victor

Designer/Architect: Art Small
Average Play Time: 3:53
Special Features: pro shop, restaurant

Yampa Valley Golf Club

Address: 2179 Highway 394
P.O. Box 1262
Craig, CO 81626
Phone #: (970) 824-3673
Tee Times: (970) 824-3673

Tee Time Info: (resident): 3 day advance, Friday - Monday
(non-resident): 3 day advance, Friday - Monday

Green Fees: (resident): $16.00

(non-resident): $22.00

Credit Cards: Master Card, Visa
Discounts: no

Number of Holes: 18
Number of Courses on Site: 1

	Championship Tees	Men's Tees	Ladies' Tees
Par:	72	72	72
Length:	6400	5886	5358
Course Rating:	69.3	66.9	69.5
Slope:	124	117	120

Year Opened: 1968

Golf Carts Available: yes   **Cart Fee:** $16.00
Driving Range: yes
On Site Lodging: no

Tournaments: yes

Annual Number of Golf Days: 210
Total Rounds Played Annually: 22,500

General Manager: Charlie Cobb
Head Pro: Charlie Cobb
Superintendent: Lou Hahn

Designer/Architect: William Howard Neff
Average Play Time: 3:49
Special Features: pro shop, restaurant, clubhouse, practice greens

NORTH EAST REGION

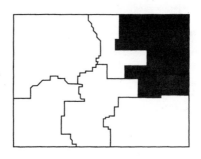

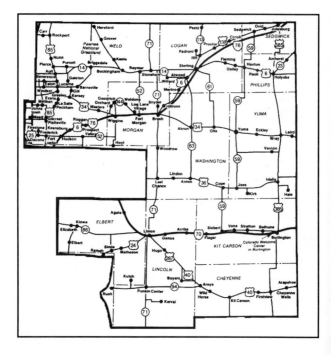

Boomerang Links

Address: 7309 West 4th Street
Greeley, CO 80634

Phone #: (970) 351-8934
Tee Times: (970) 351-8934, (800) 351-8934

Tee Time Info: (resident): Tuesday for next 7 days
(non-resident): Monday for next 7 days

Green Fees: (resident): $16.00 weekday
$20.00 weekend
(non-resident): $16.00 weekday
$20.00 weekend
Credit Cards: Master Card, Visa, Discover
Discounts: seniors

Number of Holes: 18
Number of Courses on Site: 1

	Championship Tees	Men's Tees	Ladies' Tees
Par:	72	72	72
Length:	7214	6264	5285
Course Rating:	72.6	68.1	68.5
Slope:	131	114	113

Year Opened: 1991

Golf Carts Available: yes   **Cart Fee:** $20.00
Driving Range: yes
On Site Lodging: no

Tournaments: yes

Annual Number of Golf Days: 300
Total Rounds Played Annually: 41,000

General Manager: Kenny Anderson
Head Pro: Kenny Anderson
Superintendent: Dave McDonald

Designer/Architect: William Howard Neff
Average Play Time: 4:11
Special Features: pro shop, beverages available

Bunker Hill Country Club

Address: P.O. Box 301
Brush, CO 80723

Phone #: (970) 842-5198
Tee Times: (970) 842-5198

Tee Time Info: (resident): 7 day advance
(non-resident): 7 day advance

Green Fees: **(resident):** $10.00 weekday
$12.00 weekend
(non-resident): $10.00 weekday
$12.00 weekend

Credit Cards: no
Discounts: no

Number of Holes: 9
Number of Courses on Site: 1

	Championship Tees	Men's Tees	Ladies' Tees
Par:	no	72	73
Length:	no	6166	5788
Course Rating:	no	68.2	72.2
Slope:	no	105	114

Year Opened: 1969

Golf Carts Available: yes   **Cart Fee:** $16.00
Driving Range: yes
On Site Lodging: no

Tournaments: yes

Annual Number of Golf Days: 277
Total Rounds Played Annually: 20,000

General Manager: Lance Price
Head Pro: Lance Price
Superintendent: Cecil Wessel

Designer/Architect: Frank Hummel
Average Play Time: 3:47
Special Features: pro shop, restarant, lounge

F and H Golf Course

Address: P.O. Box 155
Haxtun, CO 80731

Phone #:   (970) 774-6362
Tee Times: (970) 774-6362

Tee Time Info: (resident):   Information not available at time of press
(non-resident):   Information not available at time of press

Green Fees: **(resident):** $8.00

   (non-resident): $8.00

Credit Cards: no
Discounts: Information not available at time of press

Number of Holes: 9
Number of Courses on Site: 1

	Championship Tees	Men's Tees	Ladies' Tees
Par:	no	36	36
Length:	no	3237	2957
Course Rating:	no	69.7	70.9
Slope:	no	105	104

Year Opened: 1972

Golf Carts Available: yes   **Cart Fee:** $7.00
Driving Range: yes
On Site Lodging: no

Tournaments: yes

Annual Number of Golf Days: 289
Total Rounds Played Annually: 10,200

General Manager: Pat Wagner
Superintendent: Pat Wagner

Designer/Architect: Marty Johnson
Average Play Time: 3:46
Special Features: clubhouse, practice green, pro shop, snack bar

Ft. Morgan Golf Club

Address: P.O. Box 100
Ft. Morgan, CO 80701

Phone #: (970) 867-5990
Tee Times: (970) 867-5990

Tee Time Info: (resident): 3 day advance
(non-resident): 3 day advance

Green Fees: (resident): $11.75 weekday
$12.75 weekend
(non-resident): $15.00 weekday
$18.00 weekend

Credit Cards: Master Card, Visa
Discounts: no

Number of Holes: 18
Number of Courses on Site: 1

	Championship Tees	Men's Tees	Ladies' Tees
Par:	73	73	74
Length:	6470	6079	5615
Course Rating:	69.7	67.7	70.1
Slope:	117	111	113

Golf Carts Available: yes   **Cart Fee:** $17.00
Driving Range: yes
On Site Lodging: no

Tournaments: yes

Annual Number of Golf Days: 300
Total Rounds Played Annually: 35,000

General Manager: Rich Zulkoski
Head Pro: Rich Zulkoski
Superintendent: Jim Dalrymple

Average Play Time: 3:41
Special Features: country club, hilly - natural rough

Highland Hills Golf Course

Address: 2200 Clubhouse Drive
Greeley, CO 80634

Phone #: (970) 330-7327
Tee Times: (970) 330-7327

Tee Time Info: (resident): Tuesday for next 7 days
(non-resident): Monday for next 7 days

Green Fees: (resident): $16.00 weekday
$20.00 weekend
(non-resident): $16.00 weekday
$20.00 weekend
Credit Cards: Master Card, Visa, Discover
Discounts: senior

Number of Holes: 18
Number of Courses on Site: 1

	Championship Tees	Men's Tees	Ladies' Tees
Par:	71	71	75
Length:	6723	6459	6002
Course Rating:	71.4	70.2	72.8
Slope:	128	126	120

Year Opened: 1961, 1967, 1971

Golf Carts Available: yes   **Cart Fee:** $20.00
Driving Range: yes
On Site Lodging: no

Tournaments: yes

Annual Number of Golf Days: 250
Total Rounds Played Annually: 55,000

General Manager: Bob McNamee
Head Pro: Wayne Leighton
Superintendent: Dave McDonald

Designer/Architect: C.B. Maxwell, Frank Hummel
Average Play Time: 3:52
Special Features: pro shop, snack bar

High Plains Golf Course

Address: 5294 County Road #39
Yuma, CO 80759

Phone #:   (970) 848-2813
Tee Times: (970) 848-2813

Tee Time Info: (resident):   advanced tee times not available
                 (non-resident): advanced tee times not available

Green Fees: **(resident):** $8.00 weekday
                           $10.00 weekend
             (non-resident): $8.00 weekday
                           $10.00 weekend
Credit Cards: Master Card, Visa
Discounts: juniors

Number of Holes: 9
Number of Courses on Site: 1

	Championship Tees	Men's Tees	Ladies' Tees
Par:	72	72	74
Length:	7062	6712	5938
Course Rating:	71.6	70.4	73.2
Slope:	117	113	116

Year Opened: 1970

Golf Carts Available: yes   **Cart Fee:** $10 weekday
Driving Range: yes
On Site Lodging: no

Tournaments: yes

Annual Number of Golf Days: 290
Total Rounds Played Annually: 20,000

General Manager: Richard Smith
Head Pro: Richard Smith
Superintendent: Ivan Braver

Designer/Architect:
Average Play Time: 3:58
Special Features: restaurant, clubhouse, chipping area, putting greenge

Holyoke Golf Course

Address: 415 East Carnahan
P.O. Box 243
Holyoke, CO 80734
Phone #: (970) 854-3200
Tee Times: (970) 854-3200

Tee Time Info: (resident): Information not available at time of press
(non-resident): Information not available at time of press

Green Fees: (resident): $10.00

(non-resident): $10.00

Credit Cards: no
Discounts: Information not available at time of press

Number of Holes: 9
Number of Courses on Site: 1

	Championship Tees	Men's Tees	Ladies' Tees
Par:	Not Available At Time Of Press	72	74
Length:	Not Available At Time Of Press	6392	5592
Course Rating:	Not Available At Time Of Press	67.9	70.1
Slope:	Not Available At Time Of Press	109	113

Year Opened: 1973

Golf Carts Available: yes   **Cart Fee:** $14.00
Driving Range: yes
On Site Lodging: no

Tournaments: yes

Annual Number of Golf Days: 280
Total Rounds Played Annually: 15,000

General Manager: Gary Huss
Superintendent: Gary Huss

Average Play Time: 3:49
Special Features: clubhouse, practice green, pro shop

The Mad Russian Golf Course

Address: 24361 Highway 257
P.O. Box 301
Milliken, CO 80534
Phone #: (970) 587-5157
Tee Times: (970) 587-5157

Tee Time Info: (resident): Thursday for 7 days
(non-resident): Thursday for 7 days

Green Fees: **(resident):** $10.00 weekday
$14.00 weekend
(non-resident): $12.00 weekday
$18.00 weekend
Credit Cards: Master Card, Visa
Discounts: no

Number of Holes: 18
Number of Courses on Site: 1

	Championship Tees	Men's Tees	Ladies' Tees
Par:	70	70	70
Length:	5464	5030	4250
Course Rating:	65.2	62.9	64.1
Slope:	117	111	103

Year Opened: 1987

Golf Carts Available: yes
Driving Range: yes
On Site Lodging: no

Cart Fee: $18.00

Tournaments: yes

Annual Number of Golf Days: 296
Total Rounds Played Annually: 25,000

General Manager: Bob Ehrlich
Head Pro: Steve Thompson
Superintendent: Kirk Reiber

Average Play Time: 3:26
Special Features: pro shop, restaurant

Mossland Memorial Golf Course

Address: I-70 and County Road 5
P.O. Box 301
Flagler, CO 80815
Phone #: (719) 765-4659
Tee Times: (719) 765-4659

Tee Time Info: (resident): advanced tee times not available
(non-resident): advanced tee times not available

Green Fees: **(resident):** $10.00

(non-resident): $10.00

Credit Cards: no
Discounts: juniors

Number of Holes: 9
Number of Courses on Site: 1

	Championship Tees	Men's Tees	Ladies' Tees
Par:	no	36	35
Length:	no	2846	2564
Course Rating:	no	67.4	66.8
Slope:	no	109	109

Year Opened: 1987

Golf Carts Available: yes   **Cart Fee:** $10.00
Driving Range: yes
On Site Lodging: no

Tournaments: yes

Annual Number of Golf Days: 280
Total Rounds Played Annually: 6,000

General Manager: Mossland Memorial Golf Course Committee
Head Pro: Norm Murphy
Superintendent: Norm Murphy

Average Play Time: 3:44
Special Features: clubhouse, practice green, pro shop

Prarie Pines Golf Club

Address: 48680 Snead Drive
Burlington, CO 80807

Phone #: (719) 346-8207
Tee Times: (719) 346-8207

Tee Time Info: (resident): Information not available at time of press
(non-resident): Information not available at time of press

Green Fees: (resident): $10.00

(non-resident): $10.00

Credit Cards: no
Discounts: Information not available at time of press

Number of Holes: 9
Number of Courses on Site: 1

	Championship Tees	Men's Tees	Ladies' Tees
Par:	Not Available At Time Of Press	35	35
Length:	Not Available At Time Of Press	2906	2706
Course Rating:	Not Available At Time Of Press	65.7	Not Available At Time Of Press
Slope:	Not Available At Time Of Press	100	107

Golf Carts Available: yes   **Cart Fee:** $10.00

Driving Range: yes

On Site Lodging: no

Tournaments: yes

Annual Number of Golf Days: 281

Total Rounds Played Annually: 15,000

Superintendent: Teddy Davis

Average Play Time: 3:20

Special Features: clubhouse, practice green, Steak House, pro shop

Riverview Golf Course

Address: 13064 County Road 370
Sterling, CO 80571

Phone #:   (970) 522-3035
Tee Times: (970) 522-3035

Tee Time Info: (resident):   2 day advance
            (non-resident): 2 day advance

Green Fees: **(resident):** $10.00

           (non-resident): $11.00

Credit Cards: Master Card, Visa, Discover
Discounts: packages

Number of Holes: 18
Number of Courses on Site: 1

	Championship Tees	Men's Tees	Ladies' Tees
Par:	71	71	71
Length:	6148	5815	5016
Course Rating:	66.7	66.0	67.8
Slope:	112	108	110

Year Opened: 1980

Golf Carts Available: yes   **Cart Fee:** $20.00
Driving Range: yes
On Site Lodging: no

Tournaments: yes

Annual Number of Golf Days: 281
Total Rounds Played Annually: 25,000

General Manager: Melody Defensor Heim
Head Pro: Val Heim
Superintendent: Jerry Nicholsen

Designer/Architect: Val Heim
Average Play Time: 3:41
Special Features: clubhouse, pro shop, restaurant

Smoky River Golf Club

Address: P.O. Box 245
Cheyenne Wells, CO 80810

Phone #: (719) 767-5021
Tee Times: (719) 767-5021

Tee Time Info: (resident): Information not available at time of press
(non-resident): Information not available at time of press

Green Fees: (resident): $9.00

(non-resident): $9.00

Credit Cards: no
Discounts: Information not available at time of press

Number of Holes: 9
Number of Courses on Site: 1

	Championship Tees	Men's Tees	Ladies' Tees
Par:	no	70	70
Length:	no	6087	4714
Course Rating:	no	67.5	no rating
Slope:	no	113	no record

Year Opened: 1992

Golf Carts Available: yes   **Cart Fee:** $8.00

Driving Range: no

On Site Lodging: no

Tournaments: yes

Annual Number of Golf Days: 300

Average Play Time: 3:45

Special Features: clubhouse, practice green, swimming pool

Stratton Golf Course

Address: First and Wyoming
P.O. Box 84
Stratton, CO 80836
Phone #: (719) 348-5364
Tee Times: (719) 348-5364

Tee Time Info: (resident): Information not available at time of press
(non-resident): Information not available at time of press

Green Fees: **(resident):** $7.50

(non-resident): $7.50

Credit Cards: no
Discounts: Information not available at time of press

Number of Holes: 9
Number of Courses on Site: 1

	Championship Tees	Men's Tees	Ladies' Tees
Par:	Not Available At Press	68	68
Length:	Not Available At Press	5022	4718
Course Rating:	Not Available At Press	61.5	Not Available At Press
Slope:	Not Available At Press	88	Not Available At Press

Driving Range: no

On Site Lodging: no

Tournaments: yes

General Manager: J.C. Smith

Superintendent: Rick Gaddy

Designer/Architect: Bob Hemburger

Average Play Time: 3:11

Special Features: clubhouse, pro shop

Tamarack Golf Club

Address: Highway 71
Limon, CO 80828

Phone #:   (719) 775-9998
Tee Times: (719) 775-9998

Tee Time Info: (resident):   advanced tee times not available
(non-resident):   advanced tee times not available

Green Fees: **(resident):** $9.00 weekday
$11.00 weekend
(non-resident): $9.00 weekday
$11.00 weekend

Credit Cards: no
Discounts: no

Number of Holes: 9
Number of Courses on Site: 1

	Championship Tees	Men's Tees	Ladies' Tees
Par:	no	35	35
Length:	no	3006	2651
Course Rating:	no	67.3	68.8
Slope:	no	107	114

Year Opened: 1967

Golf Carts Available: yes   **Cart Fee:** $12.00
Driving Range: yes
On Site Lodging: no

Tournaments: yes

Annual Number of Golf Days: 300
Total Rounds Played Annually: 12,000

General Manager: Wanna McCarthy
Head Pro: no
Superintendent: Mark Copley

Designer/Architect: Henry Hughes
Average Play Time: 4:00
Special Features: clubhouse, practice green, sand traps

Washington County Golf Club

Address: Highway 63
P.O. Box 512
Akron, CO 80720
Phone #: (970) 345-2309
Tee Times: (970) 345-2309

Tee Time Info: (resident): advanced tee times not available
(non-resident): advanced tee times not available

Green Fees: **(resident):** $7.00 weekday
$10.00 weekend
(non-resident): $7.00 weekday
$10.00 weekend

Credit Cards: no
Discounts: no

Number of Holes: 9
Number of Courses on Site: 1

	Championship Tees	Men's Tees	Ladies' Tees
Par:	no	72	72
Length:	no	6290	5560
Course Rating:	no	67.8	72.6
Slope:	no	101	108

Year Opened: 1972

Golf Carts Available: yes   **Cart Fee:** $10.00
Driving Range: yes
On Site Lodging: no

Tournaments: yes

Annual Number of Golf Days: 277
Total Rounds Played Annually: 4,550

General Manager: Roberta Davidson
Head Pro: no
Superintendent: Warren Severen

Average Play Time: 3:40
Special Features: clubhouse, pro shop

Wray Country Club

Address: 3635 Highway 385
P.O. Box 344
Wray, CO 80758
Phone #:   (970) 332-5934
Tee Times: (970) 332-5934

Tee Time Info: (resident): Information not available at time of press
(non-resident): Information not available at time of press

Green Fees: (resident): $9.00 weekday
$10.00 weekend
(non-resident): $9.00 weekday
$10.00 wekend

Credit Cards: no
Discounts: yes

Number of Holes: 9
Number of Courses on Site: 1

	Championship Tees	Men's Tees	Ladies' Tees
Par:	Not Available At Press	70	70
Length:	Not Available At Press	5974	4874
Course Rating:	Not Available At Press	67.2	67.0
Slope:	Not Available At Press	111	105

Year Opened: 1968

Golf Carts Available: yes   **Cart Fee:** $11.00
Driving Range: yes
On Site Lodging: no

Tournaments: yes

Annual Number of Golf Days: 279
Total Rounds Played Annually: 35,750

General Manager: Ernie Crownover
Superintendent: Kirk Haptonstall

Designer/Architect: Frank Hummel
Average Play Time: 3:40
Special Features: clubhouse, 2 practice greens, pro shop, restaurant

SOUTH EAST REGION

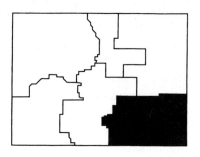

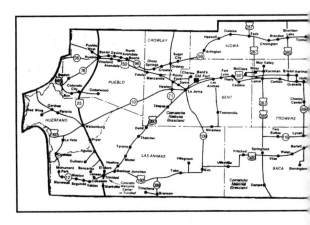

Grandote Golf and Country Club

Address: 5540 Highway 12
P.O. Box 506
La Veta, CO 80155
Phone #: (719) 742-3122, (800) 762-9513
Tee Times: (719) 742-3122, (800) 762-9513

Tee Time Info: (resident): 7 day advance
(non-resident): 7 day advance

Green Fees: **(resident):** $30.00 weekday
$45.00 weekend
(non-resident): $30.00 weekday
$45.00 weekend
Credit Cards: Master Card, Visa
Discounts: no

Number of Holes: 18
Number of Courses on Site: 1

	Championship Tees	Men's Tees	Ladies' Tees
Par:	72	72	72
Length:	7085	6627	6318
Course Rating:	72.8	70.8	69.4
Slope:	133	127	124

Year Opened: 1986

Golf Carts Available: yes   **Cart Fee:** $18.00
Driving Range: yes
On Site Lodging: no

Tournaments: yes

Annual Number of Golf Days: 240
Total Rounds Played Annually: 22,000

General Manager: Suzanna C. Chiappetta
Head Pro: no
Superintendent: John P. Harrison

Designer/Architect: Tom Weiskopf, Jay Morrish
Average Play Time: 4:07
Special Features: pro shop, chipping green, putting green, snack bar

Hollydot - East Course

Address: 55 North Parkway
P.O. Box 678
Colorado City, CO 81019
Phone #: (719) 676-3340
Tee Times: (719) 676-3340

Tee Time Info: (resident): 7 day advance
(non-resident): 7 day advance

Green Fees: **(resident):** $13.00 weekday
$15.00 weekend
(non-resident): $13.00 weekday
$15.00 weekend
Credit Cards: no
Discounts: Monday and Wednesday specials

Number of Holes: 9
Number of Courses on Site: 3

	Championship Tees	Men's Tees	Ladies' Tees
Par:	72	72	72
Length:	6592	6135	6122
Course Rating:	71.9	68.2	67.0
Slope:	126	110	110

Year Opened: 1961

Golf Carts Available: yes   **Cart Fee:** $16.00
Driving Range: yes
On Site Lodging: no

Tournaments: yes

Annual Number of Golf Days: 300
Total Rounds Played Annually: 30,000

General Manager: Prim Ivan
Head Pro: Prim Ivan
Superintendent: Howell Woodling

Designer/Architect: Frank Hummel
Average Play Time: 3:58
Special Features: clubhouse, community center

Hollydot - Links Course

Address: 55 North Parkway
P.O. Box 678
Colorado City, CO 81019
Phone #: (719) 676-3340
Tee Times: (719) 676-3340

Tee Time Info: (resident): 7 day advance
(non-resident): 7 day advance

Green Fees: **(resident):** $13.00 weekday
$15.00 weekend
(non-resident): $13.00 weekday
$15.00 weekend

Credit Cards: no
Discounts: Monday and Wednesday specials

Number of Holes: 9
Number of Courses on Site: 3

	Championship Tees	Men's Tees	Ladies' Tees
Par:	71	71	71
Length:	7010	6686	5115
Course Rating:	71.1	68.5	67.1
Slope:	121	112	106

Year Opened: 1961

Golf Carts Available: yes   **Cart Fee:** $16.00
Driving Range: yes
On Site Lodging: no

Tournaments: yes

Annual Number of Golf Days: 300
Total Rounds Played Annually: 30,000

General Manager: Prim Ivan
Head Pro: Prim Ivan
Superintendent: Howell Woodling

Designer/Architect: Frank Hummel
Average Play Time: 3:57
Special Features: clubhouse, community center

Hollydot - West Course

Address: 55 North Parkway
P.O. Box 678
Colorado City, CO 81019
Phone #: (719) 676-3340
Tee Times: (719) 676-3340

Tee Time Info: (resident): 7 day advance
(non-resident): 7 day advance

Green Fees: (resident): $13.00 weekday
$15.00 weekend
(non-resident): $13.00 weekday
$15.00 weekend

Credit Cards: no
Discounts: Monday and Wednesday specials

Number of Holes: 9
Number of Courses on Site: 3

	Championship Tees	Men's Tees	Ladies' Tees
Par:	36	36	36
Length:	3247	3125	2731
Course Rating:	69.3	69.3	69.0
Slope:	122	122	108

Year Opened: 1961

Golf Carts Available: yes   **Cart Fee:** $16.00
Driving Range: yes
On Site Lodging: no

Tournaments: yes

Annual Number of Golf Days: 300
Total Rounds Played Annually: 30,000

General Manager: Prim Ivan
Head Pro: Prim Ivan
Superintendent: Howell Woodling

Designer/Architect: Frank Hummel
Average Play Time: 3:55
Special Features: clubhouse, community center

La Junta Golf Club

Address: 27696 Harris Road
               P.O. Box 174
               La Junta, CO 81050
Phone #:   (719) 384-7133
Tee Times: (719) 384-7133

Tee Time Info: (resident):   advanced tee times not available
               (non-resident):   advanced tee times not available

Green Fees: **(resident):** $12.00 weekday
                                      $14.00 weekend
                (non-resident): $12.00 weekday
                                      $14.00 weekend
Credit Cards: no
Discounts: no

Number of Holes: 9
Number of Courses on Site: 1

	Championship Tees	Men's Tees	Ladies' Tees
Par:	70	70	73
Length:	6557	6306	5609
Course Rating:	70.5	69.3	71.0
Slope:	119	116	118

Year Opened: 1947

Golf Carts Available: yes   **Cart Fee:** $14.00
Driving Range: yes
On Site Lodging: no

Tournaments: yes

Annual Number of Golf Days: 300
Total Rounds Played Annually: 25,000

General Manager: Ron Loflin
Head Pro: Ron Loflin
Superintendent: Chuck Hansen

Designer/Architect: U.S. Army Air Force
Average Play Time: 3:45
Special Features: pro shop, clubhouse, snackbar

Las Animas Golf Course

Address: 220 Country Club Drive
P.O. Box 402
Las Animas, CO 81054
Phone #: (719) 456-2511
Tee Times: (719) 456-2511

Tee Time Info: (resident): 7 day advance
(non-resident): 7 day advance

Green Fees: (resident): $7.00

(non-resident): $7.00

Credit Cards: yes
Discounts: yes

Number of Holes: 9
Number of Courses on Site: 1

	Championship Tees	Men's Tees	Ladies' Tees
Par:	no	68	68
Length:	no	5425	4894
Course Rating:	no	65.2	65.2
Slope:	no	108	108

Year Opened: 1985

Golf Carts Available: yes   **Cart Fee:** $10.00
Driving Range: yes
On Site Lodging: no

Tournaments: yes

Annual Number of Golf Days: 315
Total Rounds Played Annually: 5,997

General Manager: Bob Lewis
Head Pro: no
Superintendent: Dave Whattler

Designer/Architect: Ray Hardy
Average Play Time: 3:36
Special Features: clubhouse, pro shop

Pueblo City Park Golf Course

Address: 3900 Thatcher Avenue
Pueblo, CO 81005

Phone #:   (719) 561-4946
Tee Times: (719) 561-4946

Tee Time Info: (resident):   1 day advance (weekdays), 3 1/2 (weekends)
(non-resident): 1 day advance (weekdays), 3 1/2 (weekends)

Green Fees: **(resident):** $13.00 weekday
$14.00 weekend
(non-resident): $13.00 weekday
$14.00 weekend

Credit Cards: no
Discounts: seniors, juniors

Number of Holes: 27
Number of Courses on Site: 2

	Championship Tees	Men's Tees	Ladies' Tees
Par:	70	70	73
Length:	6498	6263	5974
Course Rating:	69.0	68.0	72.5
Slope:	106	104	115

Year Opened: 1940

Golf Carts Available: yes   **Cart Fee:** $16.50
Driving Range: yes
On Site Lodging: yes

Tournaments: yes

Annual Number of Golf Days: 320
Total Rounds Played Annually: 100,000

General Manager: Gary Woodside
Head Pro: Gary Woodside
Superintendent: George Brooks

Average Play Time: 3:38
Special Features: pro shop, large clubhouse, restaurant

Pueblo West Golf Course

Address: 251 South McCullogh
P.O. Box 7125
Pueblo West, CO 81007
Phone #: (719) 547-2280
Tee Times: (719) 547-2280

Tee Time Info: (resident): first priority
(non-resident): 2 day advance (weekdays), Wed. (weekends)

Green Fees: **(resident):** $13.00 weekday
$16.00 weekend
(non-resident): $13.00 weekday
$16.00 weekend
Credit Cards: Master Card, Visa, American Express
Discounts: seniors

Number of Holes: 18
Number of Courses on Site: 1

	Championship Tees	Men's Tees	Ladies' Tees
Par:	72	72	72
Length:	7368	6995	5688
Course Rating:	73.3	71.4	71.4
Slope:	125	120	117

Year Opened: 1969

Golf Carts Available: yes   **Cart Fee:** $16.00
Driving Range: yes
On Site Lodging: no

Tournaments: yes

Annual Number of Golf Days: 308
Total Rounds Played Annually: 34,500

General Manager: David W. Lewis
Head Pro: David W. Lewis
Superintendent: Mike Maez, Anthony Guittariuez

Designer/Architect: McCullogh Properties
Average Play Time: 3:49
Special Features: pro shop, putting green, chipping area

Rocky Ford Country Club

Address: 91 Play Park Hill
                P.O. Box 573
                Rocky Ford, CO 81067
Phone #: (719) 254-7528
Tee Times: (719) 254-7528

Tee Time Info: (resident): Information not available at time of press
                 (non-resident): Information not available at time of press

Green Fees: **(resident):** $9.00 weekday
                             $11.00 weekend
           (non-resident): $9.00 weekday
                             $11.00 weekend
Credit Cards: no
Discounts: memberships

Number of Holes: 9
Number of Courses on Site: 1

	Championship Tees	Men's Tees	Ladies' Tees
Par:	no	70	72
Length:	no	5661	5308
Course Rating:	no	66.7	69.0
Slope:	no	118	111

Year Opened: 1950's

Golf Carts Available: yes   **Cart Fee:** $12.00
Driving Range: yes
On Site Lodging: no

Tournaments: yes

Annual Number of Golf Days: 350
Total Rounds Played Annually: 17,500

General Manager: Judy Hoffmeyer, Rod Hoffmeyer
Head Pro: Rod Hoffmeyer
Superintendent: Rod Hoffmeyer

Average Play Time: 3:36
Special Features: pro shop, narrow fairways, small greens

Spreading Antlers Golf Course

Address: South Highway 287
P.O. Box 670
Lamar, CO 81052
Phone #: (719) 336-5274
Tee Times: (719) 336-5274

Tee Time Info: (resident): advanced tee times not available
(non-resident): advanced tee times not available

Green Fees: **(resident):** $12.00 weekday
$17.00 weekend
(non-resident): $12.00 weekday
$17.00 weekend

Credit Cards: no
Discounts: no

Number of Holes: 9
Number of Courses on Site: 1

	Championship Tees	Men's Tees	Ladies' Tees
Par:	Not Available At Press	70	72
Length:	Not Available At Press	5901	4920
Course Rating:	Not Available At Press	67.8	68.0
Slope:	Not Available At Press	117	108

Year Opened: 1965

Golf Carts Available: yes   **Cart Fee:** $14.00
Driving Range: yes
On Site Lodging: no

Tournaments: yes

Annual Number of Golf Days: 280
Total Rounds Played Annually: 10,000

General Manager: Roy N. Dewbre
Head Pro: Roy N. Dewbre

Designer/Architect: Labron Harris, Sr.
Average Play Time: 3:45
Special Features: pro shop, restaurant

Trinidad Golf Course

Address: Nolan Drive
Trinidad, CO 81082

Phone #:   (719) 846-4015
Tee Times: (719) 846-4015

Tee Time Info: (resident):   advanced tee times not necessary
               (non-resident):   advanced tee times not necessary

Green Fees: **(resident):** $13.00 weekday
                               $14.00 weekend
           (non-resident): $13.00 weekday
                               $14.00 weekend
Credit Cards: Master Card, Visa
Discounts: no

Number of Holes: 9
Number of Courses on Site: 1

	Championship Tees	Men's Tees	Ladies' Tees
Par:	yes	72	72
Length:	yes	6158	5494
Course Rating:	yes	68.8	70.0
Slope:	yes	117	112

Year Opened: before 1930

Golf Carts Available: yes   **Cart Fee:** $15.00
Driving Range: yes
On Site Lodging: no

Tournaments: yes

Annual Number of Golf Days: 312
Total Rounds Played Annually: 15,233

General Manager: Frank Givigliano
Head Pro: Frank Givigliano
Superintendent: Guido Pachelli

Average Play Time: 3:44
Special Features: pro shop, restaurant

Walking Stick Golf Course

Address: 4301 Walking Stick Boulevard
Pueblo, CO 81001

Phone #: (719) 584-3400
Tee Times: (719) 584-3400

Tee Time Info: (resident); 7 day advance (weekdays), Wed. (weekends)
(non-resident): 7 day advance (weekdays), Wed. (weekends)

Green Fees: **(resident):** $15.00 weekday
$17.00 weekend
(non-resident): $15.00 weekday
$17.00 weekend
Credit Cards: Master Card, Visa
Discounts: twilight, seniors

Number of Holes: 18
Number of Courses on Site: 1

	Championship Tees	Men's Tees	Ladies' Tees
Par:	72	72	72
Length:	7147	6600	5181
Course Rating:	72.6	70.1	69.0
Slope:	130	124	114

Year Opened: 1991

Golf Carts Available: yes   **Cart Fee:** $16.50
Driving Range: yes
On Site Lodging: no

Tournaments: yes

Annual Number of Golf Days:
Total Rounds Played Annually: 35,000

General Manager: Mike Zarimba
Head Pro: Mike Zarimba
Superintendent: Lee Terry

Designer/Architect: Arthur Hills
Average Play Time: 4:09
Special Features: pro shop, restaurant serving breakfast and lunch

Walsenburg Golf Course

Address: Highway 160
P.O. Box 90
Walsenburg, CO 81089
Phone #: (719) 738-2730
Tee Times: (719) 738-2730

Tee Time Info: (resident): advanced tee times not available
(non-resident): advanced tee times not available

Green Fees: **(resident):** $11.00 weekday
$13.00 weekend
(non-resident): $11.00 weekday
$13.00 weekend

Credit Cards: no
Discounts: no

Number of Holes: 9
Number of Courses on Site: 1

	Championship Tees	Men's Tees	Ladies' Tees
Par:	no	72	72
Length:	no	6395	5376
Course Rating:	no	64.8	65.7
Slope:	no	100	101

Year Opened: 1927

Golf Carts Available: yes   **Cart Fee:** $14.00

Driving Range: yes
On Site Lodging: no

Tournaments: yes

General Manager: Orlando Herrera
Head Pro: Orlando Herrera
Superintendent: Leo Maze

Average Play Time: 3:30
Special Features: pro shop, restaurant

INDEX

(Continued on page 178)

INDEX

(Continued from page 177)

(Continued on page 1?)